Catch It A
You Can

ANNA LICKLEY

Published by Breathe Publications

First published 2013
Text © Anna Lickley

The moral right of Anna Lickley to be identified as the author of this work has been asserted.

ISBN: 978-0-9927297-0-7

All proceeds from the sale of this book will go to the Neuro Foundation: www.nfauk.org

Cover image:
Holding Hope © Lilian Baldwin

If you are interested in commissioning a similar *Holding Hope* picture, the artist will donate a percentage of each sale to the Neuro Foundation. Please contact Lilian at lilian.baldwin@talktalk.net

Contents

Chapter One	March 2012	**5**
Chapter Two	October 2010	**17**
Chapter Three	March 2012	**27**
Chapter Four	July 2006	**39**
Chapter Five	March 2012	**49**
Chapter Six	April 2001	**59**
Chapter Seven	March 2012	**65**
Chapter Eight	February 2000	**75**
Chapter Nine	March 2012	**87**
Chapter Ten	June 1994	**93**
Chapter Eleven	March 2012	**113**
Chapter Twelve	October 1987	**123**
Chapter Thirteen	November 1990	**139**
Chapter Fourteen	March 2012	**145**
Chapter Fifteen	Part Two – The Others: Mum	**149**
Chapter Sixteen	André	**153**
Chapter Seventeen	Emma	**157**
Chapter Eighteen	Greg and Caroline	**163**
Epilogue		**169**
Neurofibromatosis type two (NF2): a brief summary		**177**

Chapter One

March 2012

When I wake up, I always open my right eye before my left for some reason. Well, I know why really, it happens naturally because the muscles around my eyes are weak, particularly my right one.

This morning I could see a bright intense glow around the edges of my (newly acquired) blackout blinds and knew instinctively that it was one of those early spring days of crystal clear sky when the sun was gaining in warmth. It was, in short, a beautiful day where any description of it sounded like overused clichés. I knew that my more healthy self would have dressed quickly and dashed outside to spot daffodil bulbs surfacing (my favourite flower, incidentally).

Today though, I sighed, collapsing back on to my orthopaedic mattress.

Was I the only person in England to be disappointed to see the sunshine? I knew for a fact that I wouldn't be able to even open my blinds let alone venture out of the front door.

I had moved into this house fairly recently – about eighteen months ago – and loved it. It was a stone-built back to back mid terrace, built at the turn of the twentieth century. The street was unsurfaced and had coal mine shafts beneath it. On cold nights, you could smell the sweet smoke from open fires rising from people's chimneys.

Ironically, I had first fallen for this house partly because of its large windows and light, airy feel. Now, the blinds were drawn the majority of the time while I largely festered inside.

When I did get out alone on dark, gloomy days, with my walking frame for support, I had such a struggle getting down the uneven, tilting pavements that I recognised, with hindsight, that this was not a helpful house. I doubt very much that I would have bought it had I known what was in store, even though it would have been very tempting given its charms.

I had made the move back up to my Yorkshire roots after nearly ten years because it had a feel of 'home' about it up here. I was working for myself and so it was very possible to move the business up.

It was exciting to have the prospect of spending more time roaming the Yorkshire hills and moors around here. I could get out to lovely places right from my front door and there was an ease to living in a little town compared to a larger city like the one I had left behind. There was no need for a car to get out to gorgeous places right from my front door

This was an ideal place; it had all I needed within ten or fifteen minutes' walk of my house: a smallish supermarket, coffee shops, parks, a gym, swimming pool, library, train station and frequent buses connecting me to many towns nearby. I could jump on a train and be with my family or my oldest friend Caroline within half an hour (I would say it was a 'delightful' town but then, that's running into the clichés again, isn't it?).

It turns out that I moved at a very wise moment, just months before my health became much more challenging than ever. One of the principal things was that I damaged my cornea – two Christmases ago now – and the light has become ferocious. The term 'blinding sun' has taken on a new, much more literal meaning. Due to awful balance, my mobility has also gone haywire so that I can barely walk without support.

I have spent most of my time since in adapting my house and contacting social services, doctors and the like. My 'new life' hasn't exactly transpired to be the one I imagined.

This morning, I looked at the huge red numbers on my clock and saw that it was now 9.30am. I'd been lying there summoning the strength to pull myself out of bed since the super strong vibrating alarm (that could rouse a hibernating tortoise) had rocked me awake at 8.45.

I knew that today was one of those days when everybody seemed either to be away somewhere or busy and that I'd have to amuse myself all day. Greg, my boyfriend of just over a year, was coming round this evening and we planned Chinese takeaway and a film.

I'd met Greg on an internet dating site when I moved up here and had wanted to increase my circle of friends. Incredibly we'd got to chatting within days of me signing up for the free site although I have spoken to several people who have been on dating sites for months or even years without meeting anybody they feel comfortable with. We arranged to meet within a week, both deciding to remove ourselves from the site as we knew we were going to get on.

On the day, I had been standing in the pub waiting for him and it turned out that he was standing outside in the freezing cold waiting for me. I had naturally been nervous but as soon as he walked in felt better. All those clichés of feeling like you've known someone for years and 'just clicking' suddenly felt true.

We chose just about the only pub whose name I knew (having recently moved to the area) but it turned out to have a big screen playing a football match between local teams and was pretty full and noisy so we soon moved to somewhere quieter we could talk in. I know now that Greg may have preferred to watch the match!

I was impressed and pleased that, having told him I was deaf, he had been learning fingerspelling secretly to help our communication. It would be good, as usual, to have his company later.

Reluctantly this morning, I pulled myself upright and staggered into the bathroom feeling my usual morning dizziness and dead head. The bathroom window blind was open as I had forgotten to draw it after the cleaners had been yesterday. Sunlight streamed into the room so I blindly felt my way along the edges of the walk-in shower to the wash basin and eventually the toilet with its frame around it and arm rests like a throne.

If I looked to my right, away from the window and the light, things came a bit more into focus and I saw the chair in my shower that had been there for just over a year. There was also a bath lift with cushioned blue covers that I'd got online, chosen due to its claims of being the 'lowest reclining bath chair on the market', allowing you to 'relax and lie back in your bath'.

In reality, you could only be submerged if the water was run so high that it was practically overflowing the sides of the bath. I had taken to using the bath one night a week on the assumption that one night of decadently deep water equalled three or four of more slightly filled baths.

All in all, I loved my bathroom and how it worked for me, and felt very lucky to have all this. It was an invalid's heaven!

While sitting on the loo in all my glory, I made plans for the day. I definitely wanted to write some of my blog at some point, which I had started to keep a few months ago with the aim of letting people know more about my health and how things in my life were changing.

I wondered what to write today and couldn't really think of anything yet. I didn't want to repeat past blogs and so I tried to remember some but could only recall my very first post:

http://NicolaFrench(NFtoo).blogspot.co.uk/

3 September 2011

First One

> I've never been good at sharing my opinions because I am careful about 'rocking the boat', being sensitive to other people, or exposing myself (I only do that once a fortnight when I streak down the local High Street). But, I am now thirty-six and getting to the stage when I am starting to realise that it is actually comforting to talk with people who are confident and generous in sharing things. Having a view on something isn't going to make people run away!
>
> My main reasons for writing this blog are to share what's going on in my (over?) active 'health life' (otherwise known as 'onethingafteranother life' or 'challenges r us life' or just plain life). I also want to write about everyday stuff linked to disability and dealing with change.

If you are reading this, the first thing to do is learn about my illness Neurofibromatosis type 2 (NF2) which is:

'a genetic disorder that is caused by a misprint in a single gene on Chromosome 22. The misprinted gene will be present at birth but signs of the condition do not usually appear until the teenage years, twenties or later'

It's a complicated thing and no two people seem to be affected in quite the same way, so what I talk about is only linked to me and not to all NF2ers. Basically:

'Almost everybody who has NF2 develops benign tumours called vestibular Schwannomas (formerly called acoustic neuromas) which grow on both hearing nerves. Each of these nerves has two parts. The cochlear nerve carries information about sound and the vestibular nerve carries information about balance, to the brain. Over time these tumours are likely to cause deafness. A tumour on one side may grow at a different rate from the one on the other side. Other benign tumours associated with nerves inside the body may occur, in particular: on the lining of the brain (meningiomas), on the spine (meningiomas, schwannomas) on the skin (schwannomas). Cataracts are often present from an early age.'

I've taken this info from a factsheet found on http://nfauk.org which is the website for the Neuro Foundation and you can read a lot more about NF2 there so that you know what I am talking about in my next posts.

When I wrote that, I had hoped that I hadn't included too much medical jargon. I was kind of getting used to all the terms now as if they were quite a normal part of my vocabulary and found it hard to remember that, for most people, anything about NF2 was probably unknown.

I hadn't always written such technical medical stuff and thought over some of the other, less jargon-filled, blogs I had enjoyed writing.

http://NicolaFrench (NFtoo).blogspot.co.uk/
24 September 2011
Busy doing nothing

'Doing nothing was much more productive than people thought. Jackson often had his most profound insights when he appeared to be entirely idle. He didn't get bored; he just went into a nothing kind of place.'

Case Histories, Kate Atkinson

'Only boring people get bored.'

I always used to interpret the above phrase to mean that I was boring unless I was doing 'something': whether work or going for a walk or whatever. If all hours weren't filled with doing 'something' then I must be a boring person.

Now I see 'only boring people get bored' in a very different way.

By default, I am spending lots of time doing 'nothing' since my walking is continually bad, I tire so easily etc. Not being able to enjoy walking out in the sunshine and biting frost is frustrating and disappointing but being at home's not really boring, there's always something to think about. Mind you, I still don't like the idea that being a bit bored makes you boring. Being able to handle boredom is also an achievement!

I have been thinking recently about what is doing 'something' anyway. Is sitting reading, for example, doing 'nothing' or doing 'something' that you enjoy?

Is thinking about what is doing 'something' and what is doing 'nothing' doing 'something' or not?!

http://NicolaFrench(NFtoo).blogspot.co.uk/
2 October 2011
Chains, dogs and snot clots

(I'm as) frustrated as a dog on a chain
Anton Chekhov
(I am frustrated) like a clot of snot under a policeman's boot
Gustave Flaubert

Frustration [frʌˈstreɪʃən]

n

1. the condition of being frustrated
2. something that frustrates
3. (Psychology) *Psychol*

a. the prevention or hindering of a potentially satisfying activity

b. the emotional reaction to such prevention that may involve aggression

Rarely a day goes by without approximately 77 frustrating moments (or possibly 2893). There are the big things, obviously, like not being able to get out of the house, nip to the shop, see the sky, jump on a train.

Other, smaller ones can sometimes seem even harder to remain calm about! I have decided that I would define frustration like this:

Frustration is:

- Not being able to read your post until someone comes to visit
- Sitting in the dark because you can't change a light bulb without breaking a leg
- Having such clumsy hands that you can't open your bar of chocolate after you have just lowered yourself into a bath on your excruciatingly slow bath chair (I keep a pair of scissors by my bath now – I'm not stupid!)

- Not being able to type this blog because it's so hard to see the keyboard (I must learn to touch type)

Things like this happen so often that I am almost immune to them now but daily life is full of frustrations.

Mind you, although I am well practised at handling frustration, I am still trying to work out how a frustrated person becomes 'a clot of snot'. I haven't yet (not last time I checked, anyway).

http://NicolaFrench(NFtoo).blogspot.co.uk/
Monkeys and bananas

'We share 98% of our DNA with a chimpanzee and 50% with a banana.'
Engleby, Sebastian Faulks

I'm more Arts than Sciences and certainly no geneticist just yet but NF2 has given me a bigger reason to look into it. Don't ask me if that quote is true or not either.

In short, there's a gene called Merlin that makes a protein also called Merlin (I might have that wrong or they must have been struggling for names that day. Why not Lancelot or Guinevere?). Anyway, the Merlin protein suppresses tumour growth and if it's not working properly or the gene isn't producing it right then tumours start up. The gene is located on chromosome 22. What I really want to know, if *Engleby* is telling the truth, is, which 50 % of our DNA is the same as a banana? Do bananas have chromosome 22 and Merlin genes meaning that some of them have NF2?

OK, probably not ... But if chimpanzees are 98% similar, has there ever been an NF2-affected monkey falling out of trees due to bad balance? Ha! I will do some research.

It was on thinking about these blogs that I started to envision the process leading to my current state of health, especially my most recent experience in hospital. I was in a reflective mood today. Perhaps Kate Atkinson's character Jackson Brodie, who I had quoted in my blog, really was right that a person can have their 'most profound insights' in times when nothing appears to be happening? I made my thoughts into kind of short stories as if talking about myself from somewhere else.

Chapter Two

October 2010

Nicola had spent the night in a small, windowless side ward reserved for people who were having the treatment. As the medical staff wanted to begin early, she had needed to stay in hospital the night before as it would take all day and they needed an early start.

She woke early after a wakeful night because the room was so airless and stiflingly warm. She had asked the night nurse for a desktop fan to put by the bed but had been told that fans were no longer allowed as they might spread germs. Nicola didn't point out that with no windows and no other patients, this room was unlikely to be a source of anything sinister.

Although it was only 7am, she was already sitting up in bed doing a large crossword puzzle ripped from Saturday's *Times* when the nurse came in to take her blood pressure and temperature. She noted the time because she had expected to be woken at 6am as seemed about usual in hospitals but perhaps she had been left until last and allowed more time, being in a private room?

Almost as soon as the nurse had left the room, pushing her mobile examination unit, Nicola's breakfast of cornflakes and tea arrived (no one had asked her what she'd like to eat; soggy cornflakes wouldn't have been her first choice but she ate them anyway).

At 8am her sister, Emma, arrived having driven for over an hour. She would keep Nicola company during the waiting periods (the admissions letter had suggested having company). At 8.30 a porter came with a wheelchair to take Nicola down to the radiology department where they were met by another nurse, Paul, who Nicola already knew because he knew British Sign Language and the team ensured that he was present at all her appointments to help with communication. He would be around for the whole process to communicate what was going on.

Hi Nicola, he signed, are you ready?

Raring to go! She rolled her eyes, smiled and shook her head as she signed this.

First, we need to fit the frame and then we will give you an MRI scan so that we can see exactly where to channel the radiation. Then we will take you to a waiting room and a taxi will come to bring you across to the other hospital for the treatment itself. You might have to wait quite a while then while we look at the scans. There will be a nurse waiting with you called Sara, she knows some sign too. Be careful as she is trouble, he joked.

Can you fill this in for me?

Paul handed her a clipboard with a questionnaire for her to complete before the scan. Nicola had had so many scans that she practically knew the questions blindfold.

Had she ever had a heart attack? Did she have any metal in her body? Had she ever had any metal in her eyes? Had she ever had surgery to her head? If yes, when? Had she ever had epilepsy?

It went on for about twenty questions. When she had completed it, Paul had disappeared. Nicola was using the wheelchair now and so Emma took the board and went to look for someone to give it to.

She came back with Paul once again who signed that they were ready and wheeled her chair to a curtained off area.

Nicola's sister took a seat in the waiting area and pulled out her book, knowing Nicola would be wheeled back there once her frame was in place.

There was a posse of several doctors and nurses waiting inside the curtained room, all knowing exactly what they had to do.

The nurse introduced her to the team and everyone smiled and said 'hi'.

I need to style your hair first, he signed, smiling and taking a bunch of hair behind her ears on each side and fixing them with elastic bands.

Good choice, Nicola protested laughingly, elastic bands will get stuck and pull all my hair out!

Yeah, sorry, but they have no metal in them.

She narrowed her eyes in mock disdain and shook her head.

A different nurse came into her field of vision then: holding a syringe, his hands were protected by blue latex gloves.

This is a local anaesthetic, the injections will probably hurt but then when we fit the frame, you won't feel it. We need to numb four areas, two on your forehead and two at the back.

Yeah, OK, get it done with.

A female nurse took hold of her hand for moral support and the doctor put the needle in her forehead. It felt like something was pressing her with force and stung intensely.

'Ow, ow, ow, ow,' Nicola voiced, squeezing hard on the hand she was clutching.

Almost done.

As the needle was removed she laughed. Sorry, she signed, but it always helps to say 'ow'!

Say it as loud as you can next time! You are doing really well.

The needle was inserted a second time on the other side of her forehead, and there was more blindingly sharp pain.

'Ow, ow, *owwwwwwwwww*!'

Then it stopped and she smiled but slightly less brightly.

It's automatic. Unavoidable!

Half way there, most people cry by now, you are doing brilliantly.

When the injections were over, doctors pushed fingers against her head to check that the four areas had no feeling. Then they brought out the frame, rather like a metal helmet, and held it over her head, lining up the screws with the injected areas.

The frame needed to be secured on her head and each screw made her skull vibrate and she could 'hear' the internal hammering while the screws turned but there was no more pain.

That's it, the nurse told her, the worst part is finished. We'll take you back to your sister and then someone will come to take you for an MRI very soon.

She was wheeled back to the waiting area and Emma laid down her book when she saw them coming.

'Do you like it?' Nicola asked, cupping her hands round the frame.

'Lovely, it suits you.'

'Did you hear me?'

'No, why?'

'Thought you might hear the screams!'

As they sat there, a boy of about five or six came to stand in front of Nicola.

'What's that on your head?'

Nicola couldn't lip-read but Emma repeated it for her.

'He says, what's that?' pointing to the frame.

'Ah, well it's a special crown,' she told the boy.

'Oh,' he replied, satisfied and turning to walk away.

'Not really,' Nicola explained to his back, 'It is called a frame. I am going to have a treatment called Stereotactic Radiosurgery that only works with one of these on your head.'

'Oh', he thought for a second, 'Is it magic?'

'No, not really. But it's very clever.'

'Does it hurt?'

'It did to have it put on but now it doesn't.'

'Oh.'

At that he turned to walk to his seat where he was drawing a picture. After a few moments, he came back to ask a question.

'Can I draw you?'

'Are you an artist?'

'Yes,' came the proud response.

'You can but I will be going for the treatment very soon.'

'That's OK, I will remember it.'

'Brilliant, OK, you can show it to Emma when you have finished.'

'Yes,' and he went to sit down where he concentrated on his important task.

Just then another porter came, ready to take her to the scan.

'Well, bye,' she waved to Emma. 'Be good.'

And she was wheeled off down the corridor. Emma went back to trying to read her book.

December 2010

Nicola was sitting on the floor, as close to the TV as she could get. She couldn't really see clearly enough to read subtitles except for the odd word but fortunately the Christmas telly had things she could just about see and follow without any words. Currently, she was watching a ballet and the dancers themselves were telling the story through their movement.

Earlier, she'd watched the *Snowman* animation which was mainly wordless but she had seen it so many times she knew it by heart and sang the theme song 'Walking in the Air' in her head as she watched.

Peter was washing up in the kitchen after having served up a lovely turkey dinner, of which Mum had pointed out what was on her plate using manual fingerspelling that they had learnt in haste.

They were at Peter's house and had the fire going and she could make out the coloured lights on the fake tree fading in and out and twinkling by the window.

There were three little piles of opened presents next to the sofa where Mum was lying half asleep and half listening to the ballet music.

Nicola's pile was modest, if compared to her childhood of overflowing pillowcases stuffed with exciting new toys, books and sweets, but she had received some great gifts. She hadn't been able to read who a lot of them were from or always make out what they were exactly but Mum had explained as they opened them whilst they decadently drank glasses of bubbly at 12pm.

For several weeks, Nicola's left eye (the one with decent sight) had been red and sore and had not been responding to the prescribed course of Chloramphenicol, instead getting worse and worse. She had needed to take painkillers and keep her eye closed as much as possible.

Eventually, Mum had taken her to the eye hospital where they had sat for hours in the antiseptic waiting room full of people looking drained and half asleep on faded green chairs, staring at a TV screen that seemed to be showing adverts.

After an eye check (her right eye couldn't read any of the lines of letters and the nurse stood in front of her holding a card with a giant black F on it, which she did manage to see).

When they finally got to see one of the eye doctors, Nicola was asked to rest her chin on a machine so that the doctor could shine lights in her eyes and look at them properly.

As they had come in to the hospital at short notice, Nicola had no BSL interpreter but she could still see well enough from her left eye to lip-read some of what the doctor said, or Mum repeated it to her. She could lip-read her more easily, being more familiar with her mouth pattern.

'You have two scratches on the cornea of your eye that are quite big and we'll need to patch your eye closed for at least a week.'

'What, now?'

'Yes. We'll give you lots of drops and your mum will need to remove the dressing twice a day to bathe the eye and put in the drops; we'll show her what to do.'

'But I don't live with my mum. I'm planning Christmas with my boyfriend this year.'

Then Mum interrupted, 'You'll have to come to Peter's house for Christmas. It'll be fine, we'll have a cosy time.'

Nicola was so disappointed but saw immediately that this was the only possible solution; she knew it would be OK at Pater's house.

'Yes, you're right, are you sure that's OK?

'Of course.'

They moved into the treatment room where a nurse explained to Mum what to do and filled Nicola's eye with oceans of soothing drops and then closed the eye and patched it up.

She could see colours and shapes without making out finer things and she went with Mum into the corridor, passed the brown splodge effect pictures she could still make out and into the canteen where she could identify a coffee dispensing machine, tables with hard brown chairs and people (although she could not be sure if they were men or women unless she got very close).

Mum lead her to an empty table and left her, coming back moments later with sugared tea in polystyrene cups.

'Thank you,' and she took it gratefully; it calmed the sick shock feeling in her stomach.

'How are we going to communicate?'

She saw Mum shrugging and then rubbing her arm.

'I know deaf-blind manual fingerspelling I think, give me your hand.'

Mum already knew fingerspelling and the deaf-blind alphabet was quite similar so Nicola ran through A-Z and Mum then spelt 'We OK' on her hands.

CATCH IT ANYTIME YOU CAN

Chapter Three

March 2012

That Christmas had been so tough and I had had so much time with only my thoughts to occupy me that I had got entirely bored of recycled ideas and I'd very much missed having Greg to hold me too.

On Boxing Day, Mum, Peter and I had been to York to 'look' round the minster, have a coffee and do a little shopping. I had been able to walk by linking arms with them both to give me support from either side but had found it all very disorientating and distressing. Although I can see a bit more clearly these days, I still only have a pretty low level of vision because of scarring on my previously damaged cornea that causes sensitivity to glare and opacity on the lens. I have usually learnt to handle it a bit better nowadays, although I do find myself getting very panicky when I can't communicate or understand people.

Back then, the inability to see or hear made me feel inexplicably angry and I was lashing out at people with me almost as if it was their fault that I couldn't understand. Most of the time I preferred not to even try communicating with anyone to avoid the feeling of desperation and pent-up frustrated raging that came over me. I also felt like the more invisible the world became to me, the more invisible I became myself and vice versa, I still feel that when my vision is bad (it seems to come and go at the moment).

The eye problems had started around the time Greg and I had met. On our first date I had had a sore, red eye that I thought was infected, although it wasn't responding to the antibiotic drops my GP had prescribed. It gradually got sorer and sorer and redder and redder until I was almost crying with the pain sometimes and we went to the eye hospital where it was bandaged up. Greg was 'lucky' enough to meet me just as all this turmoil was starting.

The problem is exacerbated because, although I only damaged my left cornea, I've had a cataract on my right eye since birth and never had it removed. Unfortunately when I was young, we didn't know I had NF2 and would go deaf and later damage my other eye. Unless you remove juvenile cataracts (which are common with this illness) before the age of about ten, your brain never learns to process the information so, if I had it removed now, I'd likely see from it as through my cataract.

The corneal scarring means that I see as if through a frosted glass window. Everything is cloudy and I get the impression that, if only I could wipe it properly, I would be able to see clearly again.

Like frosting, there seem to be times when I find a clearer area of the glass and can see better but then it clouds over again. Sometimes also, the eye feels really dry and prickly as if I have something in there to irritate it. I have drops but they only ease it for a short time and then the itchy feeling comes back.

I was now seeing manageably better, particularly when I was inside and so, on mornings like today, I invariably made my way slowly down the stairs, which I did one step at a time, one foot and then the next. I had handrails on both walls running down the sides of the narrow staircase and I held on to both rails.

Walking through the lounge, I ran my hand gently along the Ikea bookshelves for support (if I leant too heavily against them, they were likely to topple over or send an avalanche of books crashing to the floor). These were full of books that I could no longer read since the print was too small for me to see but I did love the sight of the books themselves and enjoyed looking at the covers to remind myself of what was there.

I often marvelled at novelists' ability to write good books and I spent lots of time reading. When the eye damage had first happened, I had spent hours just thinking with no kind of distraction but had received the wonderful gift of an iPad from my very generous friend Caroline and was now able to download and read ebooks in large, white on black font. This was one of my mainstays.

Caroline was coming over tomorrow with her daughter Sam to take me out for a coffee. She was an old school friend who had never moved away from the area so was here when I moved back. We'd lived on the same street as kids and always been close. Now, she had been married to her second husband, Alex, for just over four years and their little girl Sam was about three.

She had met her first husband, Ryan, at school and they had married very young. The marriage had ended acrimoniously after just three years. It had turned out that Ryan (and possibly Caroline too) had been far too immature to marry. They were friends now and both very happy in their second marriages.

She'd gone back to work part time after having Sam and thoroughly enjoyed her job as a solicitor. Sam had fun at nursery on the days that her mum was busy and enjoyed playing with her little friends. We went out every couple of weeks for coffee.

In the kitchen this morning, I filled the kettle and switched it on. It had a little blue light so that I could see if it was on properly or not.

While I was waiting, I took a bottle of milk from the fridge. Unfortunately, it was a new bottle and the green top was too tightly screwed on for me. After several attempts, I put on a pair of rubber washing-up gloves and tried again. Eventually, I felt it loosen and come away. Next came the foil 'pull' which broke off as I pulled and I had to pierce the rest with a knife to get to the milk. This sort of palaver of 'simple' things happened far too often.

I reached for the biscuit tin, as was my morning habit, and took out three digestive biscuits which I slipped into my dressing gown pocket.

The vacuum mug I used had a lid so that I could carry it upstairs without spilling my tea and I went up two flights of stairs to my attic room where I had my PC.

Switching it on, keen to recap more of my past blogs, I was still wracking my brains at what to write for today's entry. All I could think of was the monotony and predictability of my routine these days but I knew that I had already talked about that. I was very aware that I now noticed and focused on the need to carry out very small, mundane things whereas previously I would have zipped through them with barely a thought.

One day, I'd like to write a book based around my blog and my life but I didn't think I'd be likely to include the tedium of days like today. Since I was struggling even to think of a blog entry, I doubted that I could write a whole book. Getting my life story into a book would be rather like turning a bestseller into a screenplay anyway. You had to miss out so much and condense it to make something interesting but still true to the original.

When I looked at my blogs, I noted the ones about what had happened recently and how things are with my health:

http://NicolaFrench(NFtoo).blogspot.co.uk/
15 September 2011
Wisdom

> Frodo: 'I wish the ring had never come to me. I wish that none of this had ever happened.'

> Gandalf: 'So do all who live to see such times but that isn't for them to decide. All we have to do is decide what to do with the time that is given to us.' (From the film version of *TLOTR* – not sure which one!)

> 'Life isn't cast in a mould – cut out by rule and line, and that sort of thing.'
> *Middlemarch*

> Like his friend C.S. Lewis, Tolkien was writing as a Christian, He was, like me, influenced and inspired

by the very wise teachings of Jesus and thus making Gandalf incredibly wise in his writings.

This year has been so very tumultuous for me but I am getting gradually used to adapting, changing and re-arranging myself.

In the last twelve months I have: relocated from Bristol (where I was settled for ten years) back to my roots in Yorkshire, I have met someone lovely (but he's on my list because he requires patience and lots of hard work all the same, lol), As I said, I have damaged the cornea on my one good eye and have spent some time without sight and now have low vision and can't see in glare.

My balance has also gone haywire so I can't really move about outside without support (It is, quite literally 'staggering'). I had gamma knife (also called Stereotactic Radiosurgery) treatment in October 2010 and am waiting for another round of treatment in January next year.

So, loads has changed and I wouldn't choose most of it but it's happened and so now I am 'deciding what to do with the time given to me' and finding there are still things I can enjoy that I wouldn't have thought of (not to say it's all gems). I know that days when I can laugh with friends or family are the best days – so I decide that!

Here's another quote I like: 'A real friend isn't capable of feeling sorry for you.'

Anna in *My Sister's Keeper*

http://NicolaFrench(NFtoo).blogspot.co.uk/

6 September 2011

The eyes have it

> 'And I have seen one, whom the world called poor,
> Walking amid the mountains of his thoughts.'
> From *Dedicatory* by Mary Gilmore

Since I damaged my 'good' eye I have been in and out of eye hospitals ever since. I've used oceans of eye drops and had surgery on my eyelids to help the eyes close and protect them.

I have spent many an hour in waiting rooms and liken them to black holes – once in; you may never come back out. If you want to master the art of waiting then I recommend a visit.

Waiting induces 'hospital flu' and symptoms include:

- Brain deadness
- Numb-flat bum
- Coffee and cake craving

By the time you see a doctor, you are so brain-dead that you can barely remember your name (and the nurses will ask ad nauseam along with your date of birth, address and if you are allergic to latex).

http://NicolaFrench(NFtoo).blogspot.co.uk/
10 September 2011
(Don't) Let There be Light
    One misty, moisty, morning,
    When cloudy was the weather,
    Little Nicky stepped outside
    Without the bright sun to get 'er

    For once she saw the houses o'er the street
    Although, with no hold, she risked not to move
    her feet
    But it was always the misty, moisty, morning gloom
    That she looked out for from her upstairs room

    What a catchy poem! Next time you are
disappointed to see a dark, damp day, think of it as
a 'Nicola day' when I will be getting the flags out to
see the misty moistness!

http://NicolaFrench(NFtoo).blogspot.co.uk/
24 February 2012
It's a kind of magic

    'And hence he must be invisible; for a spirit
cannot be seen by the eye of man: nor is there
any thing in this principle contradictory to reason
or experience.'
Adam Clarke

It often takes magic to make things invisible so I wonder what kind of magic it is that I have picked up as I'm getting more disabled? I can feel invisible a lot, especially at parties or social events where I can no longer walk around and get chatting to people.

That sort of thing was hard enough as 'just' a deaf person but now, as a deaf, visually impaired person who can't get out of a chair or walk about without help, it is surprising how strong that sense of invisibility can become.

You see someone you know nearby but can't get up to say 'hi' and they don't see you or whatever and it's very easy to feel ignored and, of course, my spirit of openness, vast intelligence and huge wit is well hidden(!).

Many people are familiar with the film quote, 'Nobody puts Baby in a corner', but if she had disabilities, she'd probably find herself left in a corner much more than she would like.

As I was scrolling through blogs I had already written, one more caught my eye that emphasised the massive changes to my life recently. It was about having finally faced the fact that carrying on working was too difficult and that I had stopped my job.

http://NicolaFrench(NFtoo).blogspot.co.uk/

6 November 2011

Pulling off my coat

> 'I'll never pull my coat off before I go to bed.'
> Mr Tulliver, *The Mill on the Floss*

Mr Tulliver is talking about retiring before he needs to physically. This year, I have 'pulled my coat off' and am finding that my NF2 has become a definite full-time career, mostly it involves visiting hospitals and doctors, seeing friends or riding my exercise bike (and blogging!). I am finding I can enjoy it more than I would have thought when I was still healthy enough to work because if I do one or two things I then just feel like resting.

It was a tough decision to face and it has taken some time to adjust. I miss work enormously (I was self-employed so able to be flexible). I now have had lots of brilliant support to help me adapt to this new state of my health and living with it. It feels quite freeing to be a career invalid (lol) and just relax into having NF2. I did try to ignore the need to stop for a while but that just made me more stressed than ever.

I'm also on a very steep learning curve of NF2 jargon and may soon qualify as a neurosurgeon (especially since I see so well and so perceptively that anyone would be safe in my hands!).

This time last year, I was running courses in British Sign Language (BSL) at a lovely place in

West Wales called Clynfyw. I had lots of fun and some very brilliant students who managed to pass the course even when I was teaching them!

My attention drifted away from my blog and I checked my emails. Funnily enough, there was an email from a past student of mine thanking me for introducing him to BSL and saying that he was now fully qualified as an interpreter.

I loved hearing from people I had taught and knowing that I'd played a part in introducing them to BSL and maybe even in starting a process that eventually led their careers in a new direction. I could remember the time I had taught this man a few years ago and all the other things I had really enjoyed about my work. Scenes came to my so vividly that I could almost smell, taste and touch them. The bits of blog I had just read over had also jolted my memories. I felt I was starting to piece together some sort of narrative that I could use as a book with flashback snapshots of my story.

CATCH IT ANYTIME YOU CAN

Chapter Four

July 2006

It was her favourite lesson that morning: hobbies and interests. Nicola had been up early to enjoy the fresh morning sunshine before class. The students had breakfast together in the largest cottage, cooked by the centre staff. There was the option of a hearty, home-cooked breakfast of bacon, eggs, mushrooms, tomatoes, local sausages and tea. Nicola couldn't face such things in the mornings and ate her bowl of muesli in the quiet of her cottage, doing a crossword as she chewed the mouthfuls.

Glancing at her watch, she saw that it was nearly 9.15 and the students would be arriving in the classroom (a converted farm outbuilding) for class to begin at 9.30. She swigged the last few gulps of her (now lukewarm) tea and put her dishes in the sink for later.

After brushing her teeth and collecting her bag, she left the cottage, noting the rabbit scuttling away under the undergrowth and feeling the first warmth of the summer's day.

Nicola had been running courses here for the last few years each summer and sometimes over Easter or October half term.

Coming here was the best bit of the year for her. She loved that the students arrived at the beginning of the course with little or no signing and then, by the end of the intensive week, were signing so competently that they could sit, and usually pass, their level one exams and communicate with her enough to joke and laugh together.

The course was run on a working farm in beautiful, rambling Welsh countryside so, besides the cottage accommodation and the farm house, there were just fields, cows, hedgerows and the odd pig roaming freely in a pastures.

To reach the teaching room, she walked swiftly up a track past more outbuildings and a wood store. The room was all set up for her teaching (there was no risk in leaving her equipment overnight in this secluded place). She switched on her laptop and projector, gathering the handouts and lesson plans she would need that morning.

As she was doing this, students started to arrive and greet her in BSL. 'Good morning,' they signed as they went to sit down in seats that she had arranged in a semi-circle before the course began yesterday.

Even though there were no assigned places, she noted that people tended to sit in seats they had been in the day before. She made a mental note to mix up the pairs during practice work so that they all got chance to mix, get to know each other and appreciate different signing styles.

When everyone was sitting down ready and expectantly watching, Nicola handed out flashcards to the students with hobbies written on them. She randomly selected people to fingerspell what was on their card and try to guess the signs.

A lot of the hobby signs were straightforward. For example 'swimming' was mimicking the breaststroke action (albeit less exaggerated than if you were really trying to propel yourself through water). Others were less easy to guess: 'cinema', for example (left hand, palm down and right hand upright facing forwards behind it and moving in a sideways waving action with fingers splayed).

She then showed a PowerPoint list of the English words and checked that people had learnt the signs.

After this, she slipped a DVD into her laptop and played a signed story through the projector onto the wall behind her. There was a man signing about things he disliked and she frequently paused the signing to ask questions of her class to check understanding, writing new vocabulary on a flipchart.

Then came the students' turn to sign a story and they went away to prepare a short presentation about three things they disliked and why.

After ten minutes, she called everyone back and asked people to sit in a closed circle so that they could see each other clearly and then each student signed their dislikes and Nicola encouraged others to ask questions or agree/disagree with the signer. Everyone seemed to have different preferences and tastes. Some disliked the rain or cats; others thought those people were weird!

One student disliked blue sticking plasters because they were scary but he didn't mind pink ones, which got the class laughing.

After the class finished, everyone headed next door to the kitchen to make themselves cups of tea and share the freshly baked cake of the day left on the counter by the centre manager.

Today, it was a date and walnut cake that was incredibly moist and there was none left within a few minutes. She and the students were quite exhausted but they had one more class, family, before lunch and then a two-hour break to please themselves.

After lunch, she took herself off for a walk in the lovely west Welsh countryside. Others went to the pub and had invited her to come along but she declined, mostly because it was early in the week and she knew that they would benefit from speaking aloud for a while and not having to concentrate so hard on the new visual language they were learning. If she went along, then conversation would be in (pretty limited) BSL. She also knew that she would wind up teaching new signs and answering questions when she could really do with clearing her head. She would gladly join them later in the week when they could sign together in a more relaxed way.

May 2006

Nicola was waiting on a platform. It was a very small station and the trains only stopped there on request. If you were on the train, you had to make sure to tell the ticket inspector that you wanted to stop there. If you were hoping to catch it from the station, you needed to stand on the platform to wave it down.

Unfortunately it was raining, but if Nicola went inside the small concrete shelter, she couldn't see if the train was coming or not and so would miss the chance to wave it down. Being such a small station, there was no electric screen to announce that a train was coming. She remembered that the rails would sing when a train was approaching but to her, they made no sound. She guessed she'd feel them vibrating if she got down on the track and put her hands on them but didn't think that would be allowed (or very wise).

Fortunately, she had brought an umbrella even though it had been a clear morning when she set out from her hotel to go to work. She had been delivering training all day: Deaf Awareness in the morning and Disability Equality after lunch. She preferred the half-day sessions because a full day was harder to fill and keep people's interest held. She never liked to feel people were yawning or wanting to get back to their other work.

Today's group had been very receptive, answering her questions intelligently and asking her questions with genuine interest. In small groups, they had stayed on the subject set and discussed in depth. This always made it easier for her as some groups would finish very quickly and she had to think on her feet to fill in the time. You could tell if trainees wanted to be there and had a genuine interest or were there by compulsion and would prefer not to be.

The BSL interpreter that she'd booked for both days was called Helen. The first time she'd met Helen, she had booked through an agency but she had taken Helen's email address and booked her directly this time.

The agency had insisted that Nicola booked two interpreters since it was all day and far too much for one person to work without a co-worker, which was normally very true. However, she had explained that for most of the time that she was delivering the training, she would be using her voice and an interpreter would be sitting idly, only needed to sign to Nicola when there were questions or responses from the trainees. Nicola knew from experience that often one interpreter would feel fairly underused, never mind two.

She had got talking to Helen and found they had a lot in common, so she'd asked if she'd be happy to work alone if ever Nicola was booked at this venue again or other places nearby. Helen said, 'of course' and they had kept in touch.

Today, Helen had been late due to car trouble. She had sent a text to Nicola to let her know but it had made the beginning of the session difficult as she usually started her training with everyone introducing themselves and saying why they were here. This time she had to put that part on hold until Helen arrived but had explained why and thought it probably provided good awareness of Deaf issues, which was what the training was all about.

She would be staying one more night at the hotel and coming again tomorrow to teach a new group of council staff before making the long train journey home. She hoped tomorrow's group would be similarly attentive and Helen had promised to borrow her boyfriend's car!

The train wasn't coming and it was past its due time. She was getting anxious as there weren't even any signs to indicate which platform was for trains in which direction. There was no-one in sight for her to ask. She hoped remembering rightly that she'd got off the train this morning on the opposite side of the tracks.

Eventually, a train came in sight and she started waving, feeling a bit silly but it began slowing to a stop and she climbed aboard, exhaustedly looking forward to dinner and a bath.

http://NicolaFrench(NFtoo).blogspot.co.uk/

30 October 2011

Defining Disability

A disabled person is:

- 'Someone with a physical or mental impairment that has a substantial long-term and adverse effect on his or her normal day to day activities'. (DDA 1998)
- 'Disability is the loss or limitation of opportunities to take part in the normal life of a community, on an equal level with others, due to physical and social barriers'. (working for Opportunities)
- 'The social model of disability identifies systemic barriers, negative attitudes and exclusion by society (purposely or inadvertently) that mean society is the main contributory factor in disabling people. While physical, sensory, intellectual, or variations, may cause individual functional limitation or impairments, these do not have to lead to disability unless society fails to take account of and include people regardless of their individual differences'. Wikipedia again!
- Attitudes are the REAL disability (ACPA on disability)

Whenever I started a Disability Equality session, I'd ask people to try and define a disabled person in a short paragraph like those above. It is surprisingly difficult!

There's a lot of debate, writing and study about disability and equality for disabled people. What started as the DDA (Disability Discrimination Act) is now part of the Equality Act 2010.

Debate centres on different Models of Disability. The Social model is now preferred and has been refined and expanded since the 1970s but mostly talks about impairment as separate from disability and as disability becoming avoidable in many situations. Disability theory is interesting and thought provoking and well worth looking into.

My thinking about Equality is that it comes as soon as everyone realises that impairment is just part of life and happens to anyone at any time.

Disabled people (like bankers or left-handers or people who like Marmite) come in all shapes and sizes. They might be moody, they might laugh sometimes, they might enjoy kissing, they might prefer golf.

People's bodies have a habit of behaving differently.

In the past, disability has been very much hidden away and airbrushed out. Disabled people were sent to the workhouse, given up as uneducable, left to beg on street corners, but much is changing in the UK. A lot has happened in recent years: people are mixing, disabled characters turn up in films or soaps, the Paralympics are getting a following and coverage on TV, for example. It's looking positive in terms of disability not being a barrier to people being 'taken account of and included'.

Chapter Five

March 2012

As I was thinking these things and reading the blogs, I realised that I had reached the bottom of my tea. It was getting cold and I re-capped the mug over the last dregs. My legs were cramping up and I needed to get up to stretch them out. Initially they buckled underneath me, becoming rigid, but gradually they relaxed again.

I climbed onto my exercise bike, which was next to the computer, to get my legs going again and thought more about how much I missed working but that I was relieved, under the circumstance, to have stopped because in trying to carry on, it was becoming so difficult that I couldn't even sleep for worrying about what I had to do and how I could possibly do it.

I'd set up my own business a few years after university, When I finished uni, my intention had been to teach but my degree had been French and so teaching French as a deaf person was a tad tricky since you really need to listen to oral work from your pupils and also speak French with a French accent. Needless to say, I changed my career plan!

It was very difficult for me to find work after university. At interviews, people would ask me things like, 'how would you use a telephone?' and I was so inexperienced at deafness that I just said I didn't know (I didn't know about Access to Work and the support disabled people can get to enable them to access jobs: money for textphones, BSL interpreters, adapted workspace and so on).

I went back to live at home, failed a lot of interviews (because of my bad interview technique: 'Why do you want this job?' 'Erm…I don't know, really.') and because I was trying to lip-read and hadn't yet learnt how to help myself understand.

I took on several temping jobs, although a lot of office based jobs were difficult for me so I spent most of my time doing data entry. I wasn't happy and was going nowhere until I discovered a graduate trainee programme for disabled graduates and successfully won a place. Among other things, they talked about Access to Work, general confidence in your ability and found two six-month work placements for us and supported us through them so that I then felt much more employable and confident.

As I got more confident in my ability to work and more au fait with my situation, I wanted to set up something where I could teach other people about the things I was learning about disability and by teaching BSL, I did get to teach after all, because I started a business and carried out training in all sorts of places.

When I was cycling, I checked the clock on my bike and saw that it was nearly 10.30 and I was still in my dressing gown. I went downstairs to the kitchen where I poured a little water from the kettle into a cup. I wanted to bathe my eyes as I did every morning.

After disinfecting my hands with dry soap, I soaked a cotton wool ball in the tepid water and dabbed along my eyelid and then, fishing a new bud from the bag, started on my other eye. Once I'd finished, I opened my fridge to get the drops stored in there and, sitting on the wicker chair at the end of my kitchen, put a couple of the lovely soothing drops into my prickly damaged eye and blinked them in.

Above the chair, on the kitchen wall, I had one of those 'Keep calm and carry on' posters in red with the saying in big, bold white writing. The posters seemed to be everywhere at the moment and the statement itself felt somehow clichéd but it was very pertinent to me, especially at the moment when such small things were a struggle. The poster greeted me each time I walked into the kitchen and I always made a note of its wise counsel.

Glancing at the sink full of last night's dirty plates and pans, I reached for my washing-up gloves and started running the hot tap until the water warmed up. Then, taking the things out of the bowl, I ran the water into it and squeezed in the green washing up liquid.

I hadn't noticed there was a glass next to the sink as the clear colour of it provided no contrast to anything so that it was camouflaged as a saucepan. On reaching for the pan I inadvertently knocked the glass to the floor. Unfortunately (or fortunately?) it hit my toe first. Unfortunately because it hurt, but fortunately because it miraculously didn't break, perhaps because it hadn't ended up directly smashing onto the wooden floor.

After washing the pots, I went upstairs to dress, opening a cupboard to pull out my black gym outfit, complete with black Reeboks and black sports bra. Dressing was not something I just did on autopilot any more. Concentration was needed to check things weren't inside out or back to front. I needed to sit down to dress or my balance (or lack of) caused me to topple over. Pulling up trousers with one hand while sitting and briefly holding the side of the bed and lifting my bum was actually quite challenging and something I was only just perfecting.

Once dressed, I located my mobile and sent a text to the local taxi firm asking them to pick me up and take me to the gym at half eleven. The gym was only a ten-minute walk but that, for me now, was out of the question.

It was brilliant being able to contact the taxis by text. I had previously phoned using my textphone but that was now pretty tricky as I couldn't read the keys to type.

Just after 11.30, my lights flashed on and off meaning that the doorbell was ringing. Social services had kindly found and wired in this device which made such a difference, as without it I had no way of knowing there was someone there. They had also visited the taxi office with me to set up the texting system.

The taxi driver helped me walk to the car. It was so bright I could barely see him as the sun dazzled my eyes even with my cap and glasses to shade them.

Once at the gym, I held out some money to the driver and asked him to take the amount needed and then he helped me to walk in to the building.

Inside, the lighting suited me better and I thanked the driver as he left. I loved being here and, after leaving my bag and jacket in a locker, I filled my water bottle and headed for the treadmill.

The treadmill was in a room at the end of the corridor and it was bathed in the late morning sun (by experience, I knew that afternoons were better as the sun was moving over and around to the other side of the building). I drew the blinds and then got on to the treadmill, not really able to read the screen but seeing enough to press the right buttons for my programme.

I sometimes came to the gym with a support worker who helped me to clamber my way between machines and to read the settings but today I managed to set it to fifteen minutes manual and increased my speed to a good walking pace. Because I could hold the bars I was able to walk quite freely. Gradually, I increased the incline and speed by increments and felt my heart start to beat faster and the blood pump more efficiently through my body, making my cheeks glow and my nose run.

This kind of exercise was vastly different to my past exertions and, whilst I walked, I thought again about my earlier years and how my illness had begun to affect me. I felt I was still garnering ideas of how to write my story although not really in how to put it all together. I recalled some other blogs I had read earlier too:

http://NicolaFrench(NFtoo).blogspot.co.uk/
8 September 2011
Ah bless

> 'Good for you, I think it's lovely that you've got mates who bring you out.' (nightclub scene in DRC Talk film)

> 'Attitudes are the real disability.'

> I love the film *Talk* by the DRC, it's on YouTube in two parts at Talk, Part 1 and 2, and is really full

of things I recognise happen to me more often than you'd think. When I was delivering Disability Equality Training once and showed *Talk*, someone said to me afterwards, 'Are we really that bad?'

Feeling patronised is a strange thing and I find myself doing it to other people too sometimes, but people are always saying to me that it's wonderful that I have come to a place or that I am so brave to come or go about day to day things. I don't feel that at all myself and I know from talking to disabled people that it's certainly not only me who finds it difficult to deal with.

It seems strange when I look at it rationally as to why disability makes for such a reaction. We just don't seem to 'get' that many people have bodies that aren't behaving 'normally' (that's the nasty word but you know what I mean). If, then, your body is 'physically challenged' like mine, why is it suddenly so fantastic to see me going to the supermarket? I understand it might just be because it's always great to bump into me but I suspect that's not the reasoning!

Perhaps everyone has a built in 'bless!' response like when you see a wounded animal or a miniature teddy with an ear missing?

Interestingly, I feel it less when I can get out on my own (In dark light I can manage bits of shopping, etc with my walking frame for support as long as I know where things are and don't need to talk to anyone!). If I am out with assistance (family, friends or support worker), I seem to notice the condescension a lot more. It might be because I look so young and people think I'm twelve, out with Mum! It might be because people feel nervous that they won't be able to communicate with me or that the person I am with is my only channel of communication. Or, it might be that people are thinking none of these things but it's me thinking them?

Needing to be with someone is such a very hard adjustment. Perhaps I project things onto others because I feel awkward? Or maybe it's a bit of both?

It's really weird though, whatever the explanation and hard to get used to and I go back to the quote before that 'real friends are incapable of feeling sorry for you' and realise how much I love those kind of friends! (Bless 'em! lol)

http://NicolaFrench(NFtoo).blogspot.co.uk/

11 September 2011

Independent dependence

'As I said, men value their independence in a weird way, above practically everything.'

George Weinberg

'Communication is a continual balancing act, juggling the conflicting needs for intimacy and independence. To survive in the world, we have to act in concert with others, but to survive as

ourselves, rather than simply as cogs in a wheel, we have to act alone.'
Deborah Tannen

'I do need my independence. I have to have that.'
Carol Vorderman

Since 'the tumolt', I get a lot of support from people. When it all first started to happen, Mum and I spent months in limbo, stressfully not sure where to turn or what to do but when we finally got in touch with the right people at the Social Services, I have support three or four days a week so that I can continue living in my house but have help dealing with things I find difficult to manage like shopping, reading my mail, paying bills or just getting out of the house.

It's a funny dynamic and very hard to adjust to because, although the people I see work to encourage 'independent living', I'm aware it is really dependence in that it would be very hard to manage without it. I call my current state 'independent dependence'. It is possible to still be independent in spirit even when your body makes you need support and be dependent. However, it takes a lot to learn to feel that way and I don't always.

I have talked to disabled people, particularly people born with impairments, who feel very wrapped in cotton wool and suffocated by people's needs to 'look after' them like injured creatures and find it very tough to develop their own sense of being independent.

I notice a difference if I go out shopping, for example and have somebody who can interpret so that I am able to act for myself, choose and ask questions or if someone is doing it on my behalf, perhaps not choosing what I would choose or leaving me feeling left out or excluded from the transaction and a bit of a useless blob.

I can see if that had been an experience from early childhood, it becomes very difficult to think it ever possible not to need other people to do and decide things for you and not with you.

That I call 'learned dependence' and the longer it goes on for, the more people think they need someone to do it for them or a third party thinks that only the 'carer' is competent and approachable. It is very much a vicious cycle. Independence doesn't just happen it needs to be learned and encouraged.

All I know is that, for me, when I need help, there is a huge difference between being told not to worry as someone else will do it for me and a support worker saying, 'OK, no problem, tell me how I can help with that' (sometimes, the biggest help is for someone to do it for me – !! – but being ASKED is the main thing). That way, I still feel independent and in the driver's seat even though I need lots of help. I also think others see practical support like that and respond more positively to the disabled person.

We used to talk about this kind of thing (what makes a person independent/dependent?) in tutorials when I was doing subsidiary philosophy at Uni. There are so many sides to everything and, in the end you get so tied in knots that even trying to define independence becomes impossible!

Chapter Six

April 2001

Nicola felt good in her new navy-and-white running vest and shorts. As she sipped her free bottle of Volvic she looked around at everyone animating the expanse of grass in the park. Runners in professional get-up or fancy dress and their friends and family holding coats and bags, sipping tea. There was an undercurrent of anticipation.

She made her way to her designated starting area. On her application form, she had estimated a finish time of 5 hours. Having never run the distance before she had no real idea and was now aiming for a 4 hr 30 minute finish. She felt positive as she had been training for almost a year, running about thirty miles a week recently including hill work, long distance slogs, sprints and off-road running. Her body was leaner and more muscular. She was disappointed to be standing next to a womble and wished she'd been a bit more ambitious with her estimate.

Ahead of her, the crowds started moving and she realised that the starting gun must have gone off. They walked en mass towards the start line and she set her watch as they crossed it, managing to break into a run.

After all her training, the first twelve miles went by easily enough; there were lots of drink stations and showers that you could run through if you chose to. Nothing hurt and four- or five-people thick crowds of cheering supporters lined the streets, increasing as they passed various famous landmarks.

The next six miles were really tough as she was getting tired and there was the realisation that they'd only just passed the halfway mark. They were now running through unknown, less supported streets so there was less to distract her from thinking about the effort. Luckily her watch showed that she was on track for her target time so she pressed on, picking up an energy drink at the next drinks station.

Eventually, they got back to densely crowded areas and beautiful sights and by the time they were running along the Embankment towards Buckingham Palace, she was running on adrenaline more than muscle power. Rounding the bend she was able to see the finish line and produce a final, heroic sprint to cross the line in 4 hours and 36 minutes. The iconic silver foil was wrapped round her shoulders as the mammoth achievement began to sink in.

June 2004

Nicola saw overhead strip lighting above her and her head was pounding. This must be a bad dream, which made it OK and she closed her eyes again. After an unidentified amount of time, she reopened them and the thought came to her, 'Wouldn't it be awful if this was real?' Her eyes closed.

More time passed and then she began to remember where she was and why: she had had surgery on her left-sided acoustic. This was real.

Her left eye was sore because the nerves around it didn't feed the muscles enough to allow it to close fully and it was getting dry.

The trolley she was on came to a stop and she felt herself being hoisted, bottom sheets and all, from one bed to another. She wanted to ask for her eye ointment but when she tried to speak, no sound came out. She lay back and closed her eyes again.

She felt someone get hold of her hand, her eye was still hurting but she couldn't bring herself to form a sentence or a clear intelligible thought and so she signed pain near her eye and managed to make a noise like 'ow' and then signed a squeezing action over her eye.

What she didn't realise was that nobody knew about the eye ointment she used or really seemed to understand. She fell asleep again.

Each time she woke, her head was throbbing but a nurse had finally made her understand that a button on her chest released morphine into her system and made the pain stop instantly. She pressed it like a junkie.

She tried lifting her head to see what was around her but couldn't, it felt like lead.

Four days later, Nicola was propped up in bed on plenty of pillows. She had been moved from ICU onto the high-dependency ward. She was eating her breakfast of Weetabix (two) and drinking tepid tea whilst looking around the ward. In the bed next to her was an older man who appeared to be asleep, on the other side faded floral curtains were drawn around the bed, concealing the occupant.

She had been woken at 6am by her favourite nurse who had signed 'good morning'; she had level two signing. In all the four previous times that Nicola had had major surgery, no-one had signed and it made a difference.

She had taken Nicola's blood pressure and temperature and asked her if she knew where she was and what day it was.

Hospital, no idea, Nicola signed.

It's Thursday. You can wash your hair today; someone will come to give you a bath.

Nicola grinned; she could feel congealed blood still in her hair and felt itchy. Some strength was returning to her vocal chords but she still found it hard work to string any sentences together.

You are doing amazingly, the nurse signed, after only four days it's amazing to see you sitting up and eating.

After her breakfast was cleared, two nurses came with a wheelchair to take her to the bathroom that was off the side of the ward. It would take all their strength to help lift her from the bed and into the chair. She swung her legs over the side of the bed and one of them put her slippers on for her and she voiced the word 'thank you'.

They stood either side of her and supported her by the armpits, lifting her up and turning her to the chair. Nicola fell into it and they unhooked her drip, leaving it by the bed. Nicola still had the needle in the back of her hand so that she could be reconnected on return.

Once in the bathroom, one of them asked if she would like a bath or a shower.

'Shower.'

'Do you need the loo?' Nicola's catheter had been removed that morning too. She didn't really need the loo yet after only half a cup of tea, so she shook her head no and they hoisted her up to sit on the chair in the shower before pulling off her slippers and helping her lift her nightie over her head.

'Right, tell me if the water's the right temperature.'

Nicola gave the thumbs up and held the proffered flannel they had brought from the cabinet beside her bed over her eyes and slightly tipped her head back. She felt the nurse massaging shampoo (also magically brought from her bedside) into her hair and felt the suds running down her neck, it was bliss.

When the nurses had shampooed and conditioned her hair, they handed her the wetted flannel and a bottle of lemon-scented shower gel.

'Do you want to wash yourself?'

She took the bottle and shook it upside down to bring the gel near to the top of the bottle before she opened it, knowing that shaking an open bottle might make it spill out everywhere

'The lid's still on,' the nurse laughed, thinking Nicola wasn't aware of this.

I know, she thought but couldn't get the strength to explain what she was doing but felt a bit annoyed all the same that she couldn't communicate her reasoning rather than leaving the nurses thinking she hadn't realised.

After the shower, they talcum-powdered her, let her clean her teeth and wheeled her back to the ward feeling some way to normality.

CATCH IT ANYTIME YOU CAN

Chapter Seven

March 2012

It was while I was walking on the treadmill with these ideas in my head that I started more earnestly to formulate my ideas for a book after all. All these memories that were bombarding me today would be a start. I had a re-think about including something of my present days so that the repetitive language, tone and action could be set against more vivid snapshots of my past memories. I was still thinking about this when my treadmill programme ended and I staggered over to the weight room, holding on to the walls for support.

I was still thinking about the cycle my life seemed to have taken so far with surgeries, ill health and hospitals interspersed by things that, though I couldn't now replicate, I will never forget and I felt so glad and fortunate to have had chance to do so whilst I could.

After my workout, I had arranged for the taxi to pick me up from the gym after an hour. When we got back to my house, the driver helped me to my front door and I held on to one of the metal handles the social services had fitted at either side of the door and felt for the keyhole under the handle, I then ran the key along my teeth to check which way was up before putting it into the socket. It had taken me a while to develop this technique and sometimes I fumbled around for some time before I got the key in the lock (usually when it was pouring with rain and/or freezing cold) but this time I got it right and it slipped in effortlessly.

The house seemed extra dark with the blinds drawn after I stepped in from the sunshine but very soon my vision came more into focus and I was relieved to see things clearly again.

I threw my bag on the table inside the door and decided to get lunch. My favourite 'easy lunch' was currently two hot cross buns (lightly toasted, lots of butter), a banana and a cup of tea. Once it was all ready, I carried things one by one into the lounge as I spilled anything if I tried to hold two things at once.

I sat on my sofa which I'd drawn near to my large screen TV so that I could see enough to read most of the subtitles. I switched on the news while I ate. Syria was in turmoil, there were problems with potholes on British roads. The weather may be overcast tomorrow.

When I'd finished and made the reverse journey with my empty pots to the kitchen sink, I went upstairs to the bedroom to fetch the washing from my clothes basket. Since the muscles around my mouth had started to lose their strength, I seemed to get through an enormous amount of clothes because I dribbled tea, toothpaste and food down my front all the time.

If I remembered, I would put on an old hooded sweatshirt to catch the drips and this I washed every so often but relaxed because most of the time it was dirty anyway.

I did sometimes forget or not bother to fetch it if I'd left it upstairs or forego it if I was with company and so my clothes mounted up. I sat on the floor next to the basket and pulled out the dirty laundry; using the largest towel I wrapped the rest in a bundle for easy carriage.

At the top of the stairs, I threw everything down ahead of me so that I could safely descend, holding the rails to then retrieve it from where the bundle had fallen, still secure, and carried it to the kitchen.

From the cupboard, I took out a bottle of in-wash gel and squeezed some into the cap to throw in with the washing. At first I missed, due to my poor depth perception, and felt the gel cooling my hand but then I adjusted and saw it filling the measuring hole and put it in the washer.

I went back upstairs to my bedroom to get the Neuro-4 face machine I needed to attach to my facial muscles every day for an hour and a half to allow them to be stimulated by electrical impulses mimicking those of my less active nerves. I noticed a sock on the floor that had fallen from my clothes bundle and missed the wash. Sighing, I threw it back in the basket.

The machine was hard work to attach, requiring each of the eight electrodes to be gelled and taped in place on my face. I knew that if I tried to do anything requiring movement, it would fall off and so I climbed into bed, fully clothed and attached it there. Turning it on, I needed to adjust the sliders until I could feel slight taps from the electrodes. If I slid them too high, the tapping was violently harsh.

I turned out the light and lay back with my eyes closed and relaxed in the warmth of my duvet. As I closed my eyes, I started to think more about my book ideas and things that I'd like to include. I tried to match blog posts with events from my life to complement each other.

I was tired and knew for a fact that I'd never have abided lying in bed for a good part of the afternoon in the past when

I was more energetic. But now memory after vivid memory swam over me as I lay back on the pillows.

http://NicolaFrench(NFtoo).blogspot.co.uk/
13 February 2012
And here comes Meningioma…

> Since my second round of Radiosurgery (gamma knife) last month I have been having increased trouble with my balance, headaches, fatigue, weight loss (that one's not such a bad thing!).
>
> When I had the treatment, everything residing in my head (except my brain, which is plenty big enough already obviously ☺) swelled up and made me really ill. I have a panoply of tumours at the moment – vestibular schwannoma (sometimes called an acoustic neuroma), cerebello pontine angle (that name refers to the positioning rather than a tumour type, really, but I like how it sounds) and meningioma. One day I will have a string of race horses with those names and the commentators can have fun!
>
> It's too early to know if the gamma knife has had the desired effect in killing off the centre of the tumours but it is hoped that it will and that the swelling may reduce causing my symptoms to ease. Having swelling is not so swell as all that.

http://NicolaFrench(NFtoo).blogspot.co.uk/

24 February 2012

Gremlins and Despair

'I think therefore I am.'

Rene Descartes

'I was visited by Despair, who tried to entice me onto his path of destruction.'

Hazel Rolston, *Beyond the Edge*

'Maybe if God gives you a handicap, he makes sure you have a few extra doses of humour to take the edge off.'

Jodi Picoult, *My Sister's Keeper*

I meant to write about Depression for World Mental Health Day on October 10th but forgot. However, funnily enough, I am more in a position now to blog about mental health because I'm feeling low myself.

Mental Health to me is just as disabling, if not more so, than physical health because it is very hard to distance yourself from it and look at it objectively as an illness. People also feel ashamed of it and others think they should 'pull themselves together' instead of acknowledging it.

For me, the objectivity is easier at low times and I can see that feeling low or run down or overcome is partly a gremlin. Often, when I get tired and everything is harder to do, I feel these health challenges of mine are getting too much but I can see it's a gremlin and can tell him to shut up and get lost! I have to know these times are inevitable and healthy really so I just roll with them and ride them out.

It's very easy to get mired in the regret of things. Small, everyday things like sitting in the sun with a book, chatting with a friend on the 'phone, putting on a CD of Elgar's cello concerto while I am relaxing in the bath. There are bigger things, too, sometimes my womb aches for a baby that I know I won't have, for example (I will write a whole other blog about that and relationships) but I know without doubt that it is not helping anyone for me to get mired in regret. The person to be hurt most by it is myself anyway.

On the other hand, difficult times, feeling desperate, can be more like having Despair on your shoulder. My friend Hazel Rolston wrote a very honest account of her great struggle with 'him' through post-natal depression in her book *Beyond the Edge.*

When I am feeling down, it's more difficult not to mourn the loss of things but I do usually manage to shoo the thoughts away.

Makes me get my philosopher's hat on and agree with Descartes that mental health is much more personal and just as inescapable as physical illness. Your thinking really can define you and that can also be why everybody has a different life experience even with the same illness and challenges.

http://NicolaFrench(NFtoo).blogspot.co.uk/
Falling
'The course of true love never runs smoothly.'

About half of all NF2's are 'New' in as much as there is no family link – these are called 'founders'. It's a fault in a gene that happened as cells were dividing when the patient was just hours or weeks old.

If you have NF2 each of your children has a 50% chance of inheriting the gene.

Finding a partner is a minefield for anyone but for a disabled person it can seem doubly hard. Many people lack confidence in themselves or lack opportunities to meet people and wheedle out someone they can 'click' with.

The Internet gives a lot of opportunity for disabled people to get chatting to others when they are often less likely to strike up conversation naturally. You do have to be very careful, of course and develop a thick skin against people who will scarper at any mention of illness or disability or people who seem to have a weird fetish with disability ('I always wanted to see what it's like to have sex with blind man', that kind of thing).

When and if you do find love, a relationship can be difficult. I know I feel disappointed that I can't do 'normal' things like going to the seaside or on a country walk and sometimes feel oddly like I can't be a 'normal' girlfriend. I watch other people's relationships and feel somehow I am not able to offer as much as other people.

However, I know this is all how I feel which is not necessarily at all how others feel nor is it how I feel all the time.

With NF2, the issue of having children is very difficult. There is a 50% chance of passing it on genetically and I know people who, immediately on discovering their NF2, have sworn off having kids so as not to pass it on. I know many others who have had children (some aware of their own NF2 and others not). Personally, I have always said that I would rather be here than not, with or without NF2, but then seeing a child in ICU with tubes everywhere after their fourth major surgery and knowing you passed on NF2 is something I can't imagine and I guess if I was seriously considering getting pregnant, it would take a lot more thinking about and talking through.

There's also the thing that some types of tumours (meningiomas) are more likely to grow during pregnancy with direct risk to your own health and how fit you would be to bring up a child after they are born.

For myself, I know that now my health has deteriorated, I would not have the energy or resources (I'd probably drop the baby in a bath in the first five minutes!) but I am glad that when

I was younger and in better health I never faced the question of being a mum or not.

There are more questions like, 'does deciding not to have children mean that you are somehow judging your own life as a 'dud' life?', 'Is having kids selfish?', 'Is not having kids selfish by denying someone a chance of life?'!! Far-fetched questions maybe, but full of ethical conundrums for the philosophy undergrads to discuss!

There's all sorts of stuff to think about with relationships: the course of true love never runs smoothly I know, but for disabled people I think it can be like trying to run on a bouncy castle, perhaps that's why they call it *falling* in love?

CATCH IT ANYTIME YOU CAN

Chapter Eight

February 2000

Everyone on the raft suddenly went still and started to point at Nicola in an urgent kind of way and she turned to look at André for a clue as to why.

There's a spider on your hat, he signed, take your hat off!

Before she could do so, one of the Thai men navigating the raft swiped the sunhat from her head and shook it vigorously over the water, handing it back with a sheepish smile.

'Thanks,' she said, 'thank-you.'

Was it big? She signed to André.

No, tiny but probably deadly.

Ha, yes, thanks!

It's gone now.

A slightly shaken Nicola went back to marvelling at the view on the river, with its murky brown waters with lush green picture-frame borders broken by small riverside homes and people or donkeys struggling with heavy looking loads.

The sun was getting hot but it was cooler here on the river; the raft was so low in the water that she could feel her bum and legs submerged in it. She momentarily worried about the hidden money belt she wore round her waist and knew it was getting damp. The passport and cash she carried in there might need to be laid out to dry in the sun later.

It had been a surreal kind of day as only yesterday they had landed at the northern Thai city airport after an eighteen-hour flight in a cramped, uncomfortable plane. Getting a taxi to the centre of town, they had suddenly found themselves in a tropically hot, chaotic street where cars, trucks, rickshaws, bicycles and pedestrians all fought for a route along or across the four lanes of traffic.

They got their bearings by checking the street name but couldn't find the hostel recommended by their Lonely Planet guide but they spotted one on the other side of the road and, being desperate to dump their weighty backpacks, they gambled on crossing and dodged out a path through the traffic.

The hostel was set away from the street with a shady courtyard and they were shown to a room with its own bathroom, which turned out to be what UK interior designers would fashionably call a wet room; but when they later tried to shower, the water didn't drain away for hours so that they had to wade over to the toilet that had a hose next to it instead of paper.

In the strange, shabby, stifling room, they had been keen to explore and walk around, backpack free, but Nicola had lain down on her bed and instantly fallen asleep for what turned out to be about three hours. On waking and changing clothes, they could only go out for the evening to get something to eat and find their bearings a bit more.

They'd found an open air market area with a smart looking restaurant and eaten fishcakes and drunk Tiger beer, not yet being acquainted with many of the things on the menu. Later they would get more accustomed to ordering cheap, street food from the side of the road.

They had spotted lots of places with photo displays of various trips they offered and had loved the look of a jungle trip in the mountains surrounding the city involving an elephant ride and then a raft along the river. As they were short of time in the city, they had booked there and then for tomorrow.

In the morning, after breakfasting at the café next to the hostel where they ate banana pancakes feeling like it was 'the done thing' they met at the 'agency' (a small kiosk). At 10am, still feeling jet lagged and culture shocked, they had been driven in a rickety van to the edge of the jungle. Next thing they knew, they were clambering on to a hard wooden seat on the back of an elephant with a young-looking Thai boy sitting on its neck to drive it along the uneven path.

They couldn't sign much as they clung on to the armrests but Nicola felt as if she were dreaming or in an adventure book you might read as a child.

Late March 2000

Nicola had had all her hair cut off and it felt bristly when she ran a hand through it but it was a lot easier to care for. She and her friend André were trying to decide which adventure sports to try. They were sitting by their hired tent that had a hole in the roof which leaked when it rained (often) forcing them to sleep in the hired car.

André favoured bungee jumping for kicks but Nicola ruled it out because no one except a specialist doctor would really understand her illness enough to tell her if it was safe and she instinctively felt that she might be pushing her luck with head first tumbling. She also ruled out white water rafting because last time she had been submerged by water when shooting out the end of a waterslide with her friends from university she had completely lost her bearings and panicked. She didn't at all fancy tumbling out of a capsized boat either.

As they looked through the various leaflets and flyers they'd garnered from the campsite office, Nicola looked up at the mountain range in the distance and once again fell in love with New Zealand.

Yesterday, they had taken a boat through the truly majestic Milford sound fjords. It had been so cold that most people had retreated inside the glass covered deck room to be gratefully warmed by hot tea, but Nicola stood shivering at the boat's brow with her hood pulled tight around her head and the zip neck almost up to her nose so that only her eyes were visible. She somehow felt like the outside air was part of the place and going inside would rob her of some of the experience. They saw seals, rare birds and cascading waterfalls.

Today, the sun was out and it felt warm; she ran her bare feet through the grass and looked at the flyer handed to her by André, it was for tandem skydiving.

That, she signed, I pick that one, definitely.

For some reason she felt better about horizontal falling, even if there would be a huge amount of air pressure. She wasn't entirely sure of the wisdom of it but she had checked with her doctors before embarking on this adventure that flying by plane was OK, and they had confirmed it was fine. She reasoned that this should be OK too and had always wanted to do it. Now seemed like the ideal time.

They went into the office and asked the boy behind the desk if he could ring for them and book, explaining that they were both deaf. He rang to make the bookings and then wrote everything down for them: times, dates, company names and so on.

Nicola's skydiving team would collect her in a van from the campsite tomorrow morning to take her to the airfield.

Nicola was excited as she waved to André and the van pulled out. Everyone was aware she was deaf and they were friendly but didn't try to gabble on to her. Once arrived, she was surprised at how quickly they found themselves in the plane after being given a court jester-like red-and-yellow jumpsuit to put on over their clothes. She had expected training and practice sessions but there were none.

Six of them sat squashed on the floor in the belly of the small plane and they were very soon airborne and climbing. Her tandem pilot, Noah, was behind her, attaching himself to her back with many strong straps and she could feel the tugging, pulling and clicking. Then his hands appeared in her eye line as he brought his arms round her and pointed to the dials on his wrists which looked much like over-technical watches. He pantomimed all the moves, pulling her arms into the positions she'd need during the jump and showing her the altitude they'd reach before the doors opened.

When that time came, they were the first pair to shuffle their bums towards the open doors. Nicola dangled her legs over the edge with the air pounding against her face then she felt a light push from Noah and they were out.

They weren't falling, they were floating. The air pressure from below and above seemed to equal out to help them fly. Noah pulled Nicola's arms into position and she couldn't help laughing whilst the adrenaline almost made her giddy. Opposite them was a man falling with a camera pointed in her face filming the jump for the video she'd get to take home as part of the package. She could feel her cheeks billowing with air and her lips juddering.

Next thing she knew, there was a strong tug between her legs as the harness was pulled up by the emerging parachute and they shot upwards again.

Noah was steering, all she had to do was marvel at this. The sky was almost clear blue and she could see miles of green expanse, lakes and greenery. As the land approached, she began to pedal her legs as instructed but far too soon, totally misjudging her height from the ground. Eventually, just as she began to feel a bit silly, her feet struck the grass and they were running.

As they slowed and the chute fell to the ground behind, Noah unclipped himself and she instinctively turned to hug and thank him, seeing the second girl land with an indelicate crash over his shoulder.

May 2000

She was lying in a hospital bed in a small, private ward that smelt faintly of something worryingly similar to human faeces. André was next to the bed and they were plotting their 'escape' to a coffee shop two blocks away (in the correct vernacular of the place).

Before coming here, they had discovered the cafe hidden from the busy streets near their run-down hostel in an equally run-down area of the city. They had eaten their way through a stack of pancakes with syrup washed down by endless refilled cups of coffee, watching the uniformed waitress chat to people they guessed were regulars who were sitting at the counter.

She hadn't been exactly told that she could leave but neither had anyone said that she couldn't and she had spent so many hours lying here without seeing anyone that she was sure no one would object (or notice) if she was to go AWOL for an hour.

She knew that her insurance company would soon be arranging for a flight home to England and a taxi to collect her from the hospital to the nearest airport and then another taxi to collect her from the English airport and ferry her home. It had been a slight hassle getting travel insurance as all companies asked you to inform them of 'pre-existing medical conditions' but she had been pleased and relieved that NF2 wasn't on their list of difficult to insure conditions and they had instantly agreed to include Neurofibromatosis in her cover when she had contacted them.

It had been a lot harder to get hold of them this end as she had only got a telephone number. Fortunately, she and André had thought to include a portable, battery-operated textphone in their oversized and weighty backpacks and the States had an easy-to-use text relay service but it had been difficult to place an international call and she had needed to ask staff in her hostel to ring the number for her.

The man who ran the place, who looked South or Central American, had not been particularly helpful nor really seemed to understand that they were deaf and it was important to make the call. He spoke in rather broken English and had been reluctant to help, seeming to be quite suspicious of their request.

However, they had eventually managed the call when he had fetched a young American girl who was working weekends at the hostel. She quickly and efficiently made the call and wrote down all the information. The insurance company had suggested that Nicola go to the nearest hospital. The girl had given its name and address so that the insurers could phone ahead to make arrangements with the hospital about Nicola's arrival.

After the call, the girl, Page, offered to run Nicola and André over to the hospital in the SUV she was borrowing from her parents. The hospital turned out to be a very small, state hospital for those Americans who didn't have health insurance. Most of the staff and patients seemed to be of Latin American descent and many of the frayed posters on the wall were written in Spanish.

Page said something to the bored looking receptionist and left, squeezing Nicola's shoulder as she went. A harried looking nurse had appeared and shown them to small side ward. She took out a pen and paper and wrote that a doctor would be coming soon. There was no offer of the cup of tea Nicola craved or even a jug of water. She sat on the bed awkwardly and she and André sat in silence waiting.

Eventually a male doctor arrived, his dark hair greased back from his face and his dark eyes looking swollen and red-veined from lack of sleep. He was rather handsome and seemed fairly shy.

'I am doctor Preejissano' he seemed to say in an un-lip-readable accent.

'Sorry, I am deaf, please can you write it down?'

I am doctor Piduncano, tell me please what is problem?

He wrote.

'Hello, I am Nicola from England, I am travelling with my friend and have an illness called Neurofibromatosis type 2 and recently I have been having difficulty going to the loo and have sharp pains running down the back of my legs, which seem to be worse when my bladder is full and get very bad at night so that I can't sleep.'

'And you have doctor in England?'

'Sorry?'

He wrote it down.

'Yes.' Nicola produced a letter with the name and contact details of her GP at home and her ENT consultant at Manchester hospital. She had stored these in a folder along with all her insurance details.

And when you start having these problems? He wrote.

'Well, we spent two weeks in Thailand and I was fine but then we went to Australia and the pain down my leg happened occasionally, usually I would go to the loo and it went away. I guess it first started then in early February. It wasn't until we got to the States that I began to sometimes not be able to go to the loo and the pains have become much more frequent.'

How often they happen?

'Most days, more often and they are bad at night so I am having disturbed sleep and getting very tired. I know I have some small tumours at the base of my spine so I imagine the nerve is getting compressed, especially when my bladder is full.'

He made some notes in Spanish and then wrote: I talk to my colleagues and we contact your doctors.

'OK, thank you very much.'

You have pain now?

'Yes, down my right leg. It is like a shooting pain that I can't rub away.'

We get drugs, they help. First I phone England.

'OK, thanks.'

When he had gone, André went to look for coffee and Nicola wanted to try going to the loo. She always found toiletting even more difficult in hospitals than anywhere else as it was hard to relax but she was feeling bloated and uncomfortable so went out into the deserted corridor with fading blue walls and grey, black-mark-stained linoleum tiles. She guessed to turn left towards the lifts and she guessed correctly as she found a toilet almost immediately.

The loo was labelled 'rest room' but it was hardly that, it reeked and was cramped. Nevertheless, having been to much worse loos in Thailand, she sat down and turned on the tap in the sink and ran water on to her hands, the closest she could get to listening to running water.

Amazingly and with great relief she emptied her bladder, washed her hands and got out of the 'rest room' as quickly as she could.

Back in the ward, André had returned empty-handed having scouted around for a coffee machine in as many corners as he could find but to no avail.

They were both thirsty and to pass the time, they played 'just a minute', starting with Nicola having to try and sign about Margaret Thatcher for one minute without repetition, deviation or hesitation. She lasted about twelve seconds. The game had got them through many a tedious wait on their travels when buses or planes had been delayed or not turned up at all.

Eventually, after almost two hours when the game had long dried up and a kind nurse had been in with much appreciated water, Dr Piduncano returned with a written sheet, Nicola read:

I have spoke to your doctor's work mate, she thinks best you go back to England. We have pills for you now a nurse bring them. You stay tonight then insurance find flight for tomorrow. Taxi take you to airport.

Nicola's heart was already in her boots, she felt the blood had drenched from her face when she read the words 'best you go back to England'. Before heading home, André and she were planning to visit two more US cities and then head over the border to Mexico where there was so much to see.

The doctor had gone, she handed the note to André

I'm sorry, she signed.

André read the note and looked up resignedly.

OK…. OK.

He couldn't seem to think of any other appropriate comment, was there one?

The nurse came in then with another water jug and three white pills.

'What are these?'

For your pain, was the written reply.

Nicola didn't even know what she was taking or who had prescribed them or what could work for nerve pain but communication was so hard and she was so tired of sitting around and so very disillusioned that she just swallowed them.

Let's go for a coffee at that place near the hostel, she suggested, we can walk from here and talk about things properly. No one will miss us for an hour.

Chapter Nine

March 2012

The machine switched off automatically after it had completed the first programmed hour and the tapping stopped which roused me from my snoozing and reflecting. I loved having these memories, especially now when small things took up my day and I had so much time with my thoughts.

Just as I completed the disabled graduate training course two things happened. Firstly, in November 1999, just over a month before the Millennium celebrations, my dad died. He had even bought a bottle of Millennium Ale ready for the occasion. It had been devastating for all of us and I wanted to do something radical to mark his death (and his life). I have always thought that my dad was generous even in death by funding such a trip posthumously. I wish he had seen me go.

Secondly, André had finished his degree and suggested that we go travelling. I hadn't had funds or much inclination the first time he suggested it but after Dad dying, André was still open to going so we shopped around for a cheap 'round the world' ticket. I checked with my doctors about the wisdom of long-haul flight and got the all clear. If we were ever going to go, now was the perfect time.

Fortunately for me, my health wasn't too bad at the time apart from being deaf and slightly off balance (although I could walk unaided). Mum was supportive and, although I am sure she had many reservations, encouraged me to go.

We did so many incredible things. And saw so much and in places like South East Asia, for example, being deaf seemed less of an obstacle because people spoke less English and had developed gestures to communicate with the backpacking tourists like us. It helped me grow in confidence again.

When it all ended prematurely and I got home, I learnt that I had been given steroids and the hospital in the States had given me a letter to show my GP so that a prescription could be issued to continue the course. I also had an MRI scan which showed that the tumours at the base of my spine had grown slightly but doctors decided not to do surgery straightaway and most importantly for me, assured me that the many hours of flying and even the parachute jump would not have been the cause of the growth, it was just one of those things with NF2.

Back to reality, I needed to do one more half-hour programme of my face machine and so reset it and sat up in bed to read a book on my iPad.

My ears were ringing loudly and I tried to ignore the noise but instead of concentrating on my book, my mind started wandering again to past blogs and stories I remembered.

http://NicolaFrench(NFtoo).blogspot.co.uk/
October 2011
Miniature Jukeboxes

I try to close my flappy wax ears shut.

No sound comes out but on the inside
A miniature jukebox plugged into my brain
sounds: lyrical unsounds,
A Michelle Goldstein

Tinnitus.

from the Latin word *tinnītus* meaning "ringing")
is the perception of sound within the human ear
in the absence of corresponding external sound.
Wikipedia

I'm not entirely sure if the poet is talking about
tinnitus but it certainly sounds like it.

Like many people, I have tinnitus most of the
time. I can just about block it out until I start
thinking about it (now, writing this, for example!).
Mine usually sounds like a droning plane or a
washing machine. Occasionally it beeps or I can
hear radio voices without words.

Things seem to make it worse like loud noises
or lots of vibration (sitting on trains, MRI scans
etc) or too much caffeine. It's as if my ears are
trying too hard to hear and overdoing it.

I would much rather have the miniature
jukebox, especially if I got to choose the songs.

Since my ears can only manage the Drone,
I spotted an article online when I was reading
about tinnitus with the headline, 'How putting a
balloon up your nose eases tinnitus' – the *Mail* –
so I might make shoving balloons up my nose my
new party trick (although, disappointingly, they
are not talking about normal party balloons)...

http://NicolaFrench(NFtoo).blogspot.co.uk/

Books and covers

Don't judge a book by its cover

NF2 and Facial Paralysis
The Facial Nerve is close to the Auditory Nerve, tumors on the Auditory Nerve can damage the Facial Nerve while the tumors grow, or in the process of trying to remove tumors on the Auditory Nerve. Damage to the Facial Nerve can result in facial paralysis.
http://www.facialnervepalsy.com/nf2-neurofi-bromatosis-facial-paralysis.php

Well, I have said before but more unsettling than even the struggling state of my physical health is dealing with the disability side of it. One very disabling part is the feeling of not being talked to as an adult. It does sometimes feel I'm losing myself and my identity as a middle-aged cognisant woman (I think I can say that because seventy-two would be a grand old age for someone with NF2 like mine).

I also know that the cover of my book is an eighteen year-old and I wear it well! So much so that it sounds odd to me saying woman about myself when girl has such a good ring to it.

Outwardly, as I have facial palsy and bulbar (weakness around my jaw area resulting in a slack bottom lip and occasional drooling) and due to them both do not get wrinkles or ever seem to look much older (many people would love my Peter Pan effect but it makes it harder to be taken seriously as a grown up). It's very, very hard not to see the cover before the book.

http://NicolaFrench(NFtoo).blogspot.co.uk/

8 February 2012
Making Advances

'Dropsy! There is no swelling yet – it is inward. I should say she ought to take drying medicines shouldn't you? – or a dry hot air bath, Many things might be tried, of a drying nature.'

George Eliot, *Middlemarch*

The above comments come from a total non-medic but nevertheless, I always think, though NF2 is horrible, we are so lucky with the standard of medical care out there. For someone born a couple of hundred years ago (not so long really) there probably would have been no explanation for the symptoms and certainly no treatment. I hope that in less than 200 years' time, people are looking back and celebrating the fact that so many medical advances have now got a cure for NF2 or similar illnesses.

It's just unimaginable to have open surgery without anaesthetic or chronic pain without drugs to help. Even the thought of having a bad headache or period pain without Neurofen or Paracetamol is bad enough!

I will, of course, be trying all possible cures of a drying nature...

Chapter Ten

June 1994

The University Christian Union had organised a midnight walk to watch the sun rise early one morning.

They had arranged to meet in a Sheffield park where they would walk along the path by the river that led to open fields to climb up and sit at the brow and see the spectacle.

Yesterday had been clear blue skies and piercing sun so there was a sense of anticipation.

They met at 2am. Nicola and her friends had decided not to sleep a little before as that would probably make waking up more difficult. Instead they went to the bar in the students' union and then drank coffee in a friend's room before heading down to the meeting point.

The guy organising it started talking but Nicola couldn't really make the words out as the hearing aid she now wore in her left ear wasn't picking up the speech clearly and it was far too dark to lip-read anything.

When he had finished and they set off, she made sure that her friend was walking on her hearing side and asked what he'd said.

'Oh, nothing important,' was the uninformative reply.

Nicola was staggering in the dark and found it difficult to get her balance. Several times she needed to link arms with her friend in order to stay on the path and avoid taking a swim in the river alongside them.

As she tottered along, she heard sniggering behind her and asked what was funny over her shoulder.

'You're very pissed!'

It was a second year student called Mark whom she knew as he had stayed on to live in her hall of residence. Their paths would never cross again although she'd heard later that he had got a first in Economics and was working for a large high street bank at their London head office.

'No, I have an illness called Neurofibromatosis, which is damaging the nerves behind my ears so I am losing my hearing and sense of balance. I can get balance from sight but in the dark it's rubbish.'

She thought this was a rather succinct and eloquent reply and spared them more details, which she herself was only just starting to learn.

'Oh, right.'

There was silence and then they came to a tricky bit of path where a stream crossed over it and everyone needed to take turns stepping on the raised stones.

Nicola stumbled and splashed in to the water, feeling it leaking through her shoes. At that, the snickering behind began again and she started to feel slightly tearful.

Her companion turned round abruptly. 'She has explained that she's ill, stop giggling.'

Nicola was glad of the moral support and carried on walking in her squelchy shoes, concentrating on where she was going and not talking.

Eventually they got to the open countryside and the black dark was turning grey. They sat down on dew-damp grass at the top of the hill but the morning was revealing itself to be cloudy and damp so instead of a beautiful sunrise, all they got was that dark became light.

This was good enough for Nicola though, who could enjoy the walk back a whole lot more with illumination and was looking forward to the prospect of a bacon sandwich and cup of tea when they reached their hall of residence.

September 1993

The class started at 6pm; Nicola set off in plenty of time because she'd never been to the college before and didn't know how long the bus journey would be or if she would find it.

She needed to get two buses, one to the centre of town from outside the student house she'd moved into last week and then a second from the centre to the college at the other side of the city.

Between buses, she popped into Marks & Spencer and bought a pint of semi-skimmed milk from the food hall to drink on the way.

The buses were quite frequent and, once out of the centre, the traffic was quite light in the direction of the college so she arrived much earlier than expected.

The college was easy to find. It was a 1960s building that looked like it had seen better days with peeling blue paint on its outer wooden panels and dirty, yellowish white window frames. She pulled the acceptance letter out of her bag to check the room number.

As she was so early, she found where the class would be and then made her way to the college cafeteria to eat the banana she had brought with her and then have a plastic cup of coffee and a Snickers bar from the row of machines at the end of the room. The coffee wasn't too bad and she sat down at an empty, rocking Formica trestle table. From her bag, she retrieved the book *Introduction to British Sign Language* that she'd found in the University library yesterday.

At the back of the book, there was a chart of the manual fingerspelling alphabet and information about how and when it was used in BSL:

'It is used most often for the English names of people, places, titles, etc. Abbreviation and initialisation have helped to create new signs, e.g. K repeated for KITCHEN; EDH is a pattern for EDINBURGH; PR is a pattern for PRESTON.

Finger spelling (or the manual alphabet) should not be thought of as a substitute for BSL. When a sign is not known, finger spelling a word might lead to misunderstanding because one English word may have a large number of equivalent signs. For example, the English word TRAIN translates into at least 4 different signs depending on the context it is used in: (1) a railway train; (2) a bridal train; (3) to practice; (4) to instruct. So, do not think of finger spelling as the simple answer to not knowing a sign.

It is best to learn how to fingerspell through your BSL teacher, who will help you to see the patterns created by the fingers as they move through the letters of a word. You will want to create the same kind of patterns, rather than spelling letter by letter from drawings on a card. You will find that you can read words without looking directly at the hands and without needing the signer to slow.'

Despite this advice, she looked at the drawings anyway and began to try and form the letters on her hands. When she was half way through the alphabet, a girl not much older than her sat down at her table.

'Are you going to the BSL class?'

'Yes, I'm just trying to learn finger spelling.'

'Oh, it's not too bad, I learnt it for work.'

'What's your job?'

'I work as a hearing therapist but only started two weeks ago and I need to have BSL. What do you do?'

'I'm a student at the University, just about to start my second year.'

'What are you studying?'

'I'm doing French – enjoying it. Next year I have a year living in France.'

'So how come you are learning BSL?'

'Well, I'm going to go deaf. At the moment I only hear from my left ear but it's getting worse. I use a hearing aid in it now but that might not work forever.'

She lifted her hair to reveal her aid.

'Oh, that's tough, can I ask why?'

Nicola smiled.

'You can but you might wish you hadn't!'

She began to explain her NF2 as briefly as possible.

'I've never heard of it, I will look it up because it might be useful for work.'

Nicola often got the feeling from trainee doctors or fresh new medics/therapists that she was an interesting specimen for them to study. To change the subject, she asked the girl to teach her finger spelling.

'What's your name, by the way?'

'Claire. And you?'

'Nicola'

They began learning and by the time class was due to start and they headed for the teaching room, Nicola had it mastered.

June 1995

Nicola woke up and rolled over towards the big bay window that opened on to one of the town's small squares. As usual in the mornings, she could smell freshly baked bread rising from the boulangerie directly below the flat mixed with cigarette smoke coming from Sabine's room, her flatmate.

Sabine was studying at the university too, although Nicola still wasn't sure what course she was taking. She did know it wasn't the French language course that she was doing this year but that was the most information she had.

She hadn't been at all sure how she would get on with her course since it was the final year for the French students, taking the course, of course, in their mother tongue. Here she was, a newly deafened person, trying now to sit the same course in what was, to her, a language she was still learning.

She had met Sabine only on occasion, despite them sharing the flat because the French girl tended to stay in her room with her boyfriend, Laurent, most of the time that she was in the flat and she went home at weekends. She had seemed to be very aloof when the landlord had shown Nicola her room and introduced them for the first time and nothing had changed in all their time living together. Besides, it was very difficult to communicate and understand her at all.

Today was Nicola's final exam, on Rilke's poetry and she had been revising like mad with a lot of help from Sylvan and Marianne who were also on the course. Her other exams had gone surprisingly well and she had already had some encouraging results which had placed her comfortably within the pass mark range and the marks of the other students.

She would be leaving France in a week or so and was sad to say goodbye to the small group of friends she had made but relieved and excited to be returning to England and the familiarity of home where she hoped communication would be slightly easier. The year here had been exhausting and challenging and sometimes lonely as many of the students lived at home and spent evenings and weekends with their families.

Nicola had filled her time by walking in the idyllic mountain paths that she had been delighted to discover just five minutes away at the back of her flat, reading books that she bought regularly from the small bookshop in town or borrowed from the smart new library, going to the cinema where she sometimes saw the same film two or three times to fill her evenings.

In Sheffield, watching films in French was usually no help to her now since the subtitles were generally in English and she didn't hear the French dialogue but here, most of the films were in English with French subtitles and so she felt she could justify going a lot on the grounds that it would improve her vocabulary and language skills.

During the day on weekdays when they had a gap in their jam-packed timetable, she and Marianne would come into town for a coffee and sit on street tables in the old square lined with stone archways and expensive patisseries.

Originally she had been planning to spend her year in France as an English teacher in a French school but as her hearing ebbed away, it became quite clear that that wouldn't be possible. Sheffield University had done wonders in finding a French university that had support for deaf students. She was the first Sheffield student to come to here.

When she had been told that a place had been found for her, she had never heard of the town or the region and so had rushed to a bookshop to look up as much information as she could get in as many guidebooks as she could find and it sounded a delightful town. She read of 'an historic city in the department of Savoie, located in the Rhône-Alpes region in south-eastern France'.

Arriving here, it had been confirmed to her how lovely it was. It was not too large without traffic or congestion. Many of the narrow streets were cobbled. It had a very active market and even a small castle.

When she had first arrived here (when her dad had left after driving her all this way) she had been to see Madame Grégoire at the university's student welfare office who helped and advised all deaf students and with whom she had been given an appointment by letter before leaving England.

At the offices, she was greeted by a small woman with tightly permed and dyed blonde hair who was probably in her fifties and looked nothing like the 'grande dame' her name conjured up. The lady had stood up from behind her cluttered desk and shaken Nicola's hand.

'*Nicola, n'est ce pas?*'

A nod, yes.

'*Je m'appelle Mme Grégoire.*'

At this, she sat back down and indicated a chair opposite. Nicola found that she could lip-read her better than she imagined as she spoke clearly and looked directly at her. She noticed there was a pen and paper ready in case Nicola got stuck and they needed to write things down. She had relaxed at that moment, feeling her deafness was understood.

Mme Grégoire offered her a coffee, which she declined and began to explain the support available. Other students would take notes in lectures so that Nicola and the other deaf girl on her course could concentrate on lip-reading The university would then provide a photocopying card so that they could make copies of the notes to take home.

Other students were also available as 'tutors' and volunteered to offer practice and revision sessions.

At that moment, a thin girl wearing a sundress that showed the dark bushes of hair under her arms came into the room smiling

'Salut, je m'appelle Marianne.'

Marianne wore two big hearing aids and spoke quite rapidly to Mme Gregoire in such a way that Nicola couldn't follow. She had a confident 'at home' air about her.

Nicola was wearing a hearing aid too in her left ear but these days seemed barely able to tell if it was switched on or off and people often told her that it was making an annoying high-pitched squealing sound. On many days she didn't bother even to wear it; it made no real difference except to alert people of her hearing loss.

Marianne was still talking and Nicola realised that she was more nervous than first appeared. She was also keen to show that she was 'pally' with Mme in a possibly defensive, territorial kind of way. She rarely, if at all, looked in Nicola's direction or addressed anything to her. It was Mme Grégoire who suggested that they meet here before their first lecture the following day and go there together.

However, once they had left the office. Nicola asked Marianne if she would like to go for a coffee and the French girl agreed. The small, schoolish-looking university campus was deserted and mostly closed up and so they had taken the brief ten-minute walk back into the main town. They had mostly walked in silence, both realising how difficult it was to walk and avoid potholes or lamp posts if you were trying to look at someone to lip-read them.

They had gone to the café in the central square where Nicola drank coffee and Marianne ordered an Orangina. It turned out that Marianne had been deaf from birth but had grown up oral, using hearing aids, lip-reading and speech therapy. She talked about having been lonely as a child and starting to learn *Language Des Signes Française* as she got older and now felt happy to communicate in either language.

Nicola expressed an interest in learning some signs as they were different to British Sign Language and Marianne had told her to try the *Centre Des Sourds* at the other side of the market place because she thought they had classes.

That afternoon, Nicola had walked over to the deaf centre and spoken to the man who seemed to be in charge. As she had no French Sign Language, she explained as best she could in spoken French with British signs saying that she was from England and recently gone deaf and had learnt level one BSL last year but would love to learn basic LSF too. He seemed to understand better than she understood his reply.

What she got was that the British sign for 'the same' (the index finger of each hand coming together) was identical to the French sign for '*la même*' (meaning 'the same' in English) and that many signs were '*la même*'. Seeing that she could only understand one sign, she felt that many other signs must not be '*la même*'!

However, he gave her some printed information that said that there was a beginner's course in LSF on a Tuesday evenings starting in two weeks' time and she signed up there and then. The course would finish this week and she could now basically understand Marianne and have conversations made easier by the use of some signs although she was well aware that they were not communicating in fluent LSF.

This morning, she pulled on some clothes and went into the kitchen to put the kettle on and lay the table with marmalade and butter she'd stocked up with at the small local mini-market. She poured water on to the roast ground coffee in a cafetière and then nipped down to the boulangerie to buy a still warm baguette and the local paper from the Tabac next door.

It was already 8am and her exam wasn't until 10.30 so she settled down at the table and ate her way through the entire baguette which was too tasty to put down.

March 1996

André and Nicola were sitting in their favourite pub over a pint (Tetley's for Nicola, Fosters for André). It was quite quiet since it was only 4pm despite today being 'pints for pence day' when all pints of lager, beer and cider were 99p until 8pm.

André was in his first year studying drama and they had met just before the Christmas break. One of the women who took notes for the deaf students in lectures, Hilary, had the idea to ask them if they would like to meet each other and had been an intermediary in arranging a time and place. She had been aware that neither of them knew any other deaf people here at all and were keen for some moral support and understanding of the challenges they dealt with.

Hilary also worked at the other university in the city (previously the polytechnic) and knew four or five deaf students there who already knew each other but were 'well happy' to meet with the two up at the other place.

Nicola had been especially pleased because after returning from France ready to complete her fourth year, a lot of her friends, who mainly studied different courses, had graduated and left Sheffield. The girls she shared a house with now were nice enough but had all been friends since they had started their studies two years ago and so Nicola was pretty much an outsider on no more than acquaintance terms with them.

The first time they'd met had been in the bar in the union. All the students from the other uni had been first language BSL users and were signing rapidly to each other. Nicola and André both signed (since returning, Nicola had started a level 2 BSL course and was getting better all the time) but were more comfortable with spoken English (later Nicola learnt that what she had used was SSE – Sign Supported English, which borrowed signs from BSL but used English word order). The others had all adjusted their signing speed when Nicola explained she was recently deafened and only just learning to sign and they got some drinks in.

Later that night, they had gone to a university club in the basement of the Union where they stood near to the throbbing speakers to feel the bass rhythm and dance away to unidentifiable songs. It was brilliant that they could chat away in sign when everyone else would go home hoarse after bellowing unheard comments to their friends. Nicola found it was also easier to lip-read people in a club because they tended to look at her and talk clearly in a more pronounced way although many had the slightly annoying habit of shouting in her ears so that she couldn't see their mouths even when she said that she was deaf.

Since then, André and Nicola had met almost every day either for coffee or a beer or to sit out in the park with a can of coke. André came from Manchester where his dad lectured at the university and his mum was a music teacher and pianist. They had named him after André Previn and his sister was called Myra (Myra Hess).

André was the only deaf person in his family and had gone to a local comprehensive school where he was also the only deaf person. He'd done very well in his GCSEs and was incredibly intelligent. For sixth form, he'd won a scholarship at an oral school for deaf children, which is where he'd first learnt to sign from the others out of school hours. Signing was forbidden on the premises but together socially, they had signed as often as they could without being discovered.

Like Nicola, though, he felt more comfortable with signed English and it was so reassuring to meet someone who seemed to be exactly the same. Many deaf people, like the students from the old poly, seemed so confident and at ease as a signing unit whereas Nicola and André both felt a little bit caught in the middle communication-wise since they liked English but found it difficult to understand or relax with groups of hearing people but they also felt different to strong BSL-using deaf people due to their English background.

Nicola's friends had been great and had started to learn some signing but there were, inevitably, many times when conversation got lost to her and she sat in isolated silence watching them laugh uproariously together. It was difficult for her to take part in any kind of group conversation and many people had thought her rather remote and detached when she would really have given anything to be fully one of the group.

Sitting over their beers, they shared these things again and felt enormously lucky to have met someone so similar.

http://NicolaFrench(NFtoo).blogspot.co.uk/
2 March 2012
I'm confused…

Reactions to Hearing Loss
- Denial
- Anxiety
- Frustration
- Embarrassment
- Lack of concentration
- Search for a cure
- Feeling powerless
- Emotional detachment
- Isolation
- Withdrawal from communication situations

More than hearing.

For me, going deaf was a hugely odd experience and it's really hard to put it into words. I look at the above list and identify with most of it but there was no structure or sense of knowing any of it was happening and I would add *confusion* to it!

I was at Sheffield University at the time and have always thought, looking back, that it was a helpful stage for it to happen. There was a lot changing anyway, I was emerging from child to adult and, although it was very difficult, it did mean I could develop as a deaf adult from early on. Some people go deaf overnight, following surgery but hearing in my left ear went gradually.

As it was gradual, I didn't fully realise that it was happening, I think I was lip-reading a lot more than I knew and then at times I would feel completely socially inadequate and lose all my confidence in interaction with people without realising why.

For example, I remember one day in our Hall of Residence when my friends and I were in the computer room standing round a PC (this was just before the internet which I was introduced to later at Uni, remember those days?!).

We had been laughing and relaxed but as people huddled round the screen, I started to feel unable to join in and eventually went out the room and ran away wondering why I was such a social incompetent!

Now, it's obvious that it was just that I wasn't able to lip-read the backs of heads.

That was just one thing to illustrate it was a majorly confusing time.

You go through all sorts of stages, emotions and experiences before you can get on top of going deaf and there's no right or wrong reaction or pattern you should follow. It took a long time to adjust and very many things helped me to do so (such as learning to sign and learning about lip-reading). It would be nice if there was a guide book to losing your hearing but I am certainly not qualified enough to write *Hearing Loss for Dummies*, which might have been helpful!

http://NicolaFrench(NFtoo).blogspot.co.uk/
11 November 2011
Read my lips

'When a normal person speaks, the tongue moves in at least three places (top, middle and back), and the soft palate rises and falls. All of these articulatory gestures are phonetically significant, changing the speech sound produced in important ways, but are invisible to the lip reader.

Consequently, sounds whose place of articulation is deep inside the mouth or throat are not detectable, such as glottal consonants. Voiced and unvoiced pairs look identical, such as [p] and [b], [k] and [g], [t] and [d], [f] and [v], and [s] and [z] (American English); likewise for nasalisation'. (Wikipedia)

There are lots of sounds in English that make the same lip-pattern, hence 'where there's life, there's hope' looks identical to, 'where's the lavender soap'. Here are some more similar-looking sounds:

- P, B, M (two lips come together)
- T, D, N (tongue against back of top teeth)
- F, V
- C, K, G
- Sh, Ch, J (shop, job, chop)
- Invisible, deep-throat sounds – all vowels, H, Q
- R, W

As a result, you can have hours of fun thinking of words that are going to look alike. Start with PAT for example and you can have:

Pet, pit, put, pin, pen, man, mat, met, but, ban, bat etc etc etc...

You start to see why a little context, gesture and so on is invaluable and words out of context are a joke.

http://NicolaFrench(NFtoo).blogspot.co.uk/
20 November 2011

Read my lips some more...

...you CAN help :-)

Now my eyesight is weaker, lip-reading tips are a bit academic to me unless I am with people I know well but the following list is effective for lip readers:

- **Minimise background noise (lots of people use a bit of residual hearing)**
- Make sure you have good **lighting on your face** (not behind you or you will be in shadow)
- Give **context** (lip-reading things 'out of the blue' is doubly difficult, short sentences are better than random words)
- **Keep still** – look at the deaf person and avoid turning away
- Keep **eye contact** (lots of info comes that way)
- **Speak clearly** – too slowly and your lip-pattern will be exaggerated, too fast and your words won't be lip-readable
- **Repeat if necessary,** don't be embarrassed to repeat and persevere
- **Rephrase** – repeating the same phrase too many times may not be helpful. Perhaps your original words are not lip-readable so can you think of a different way to say it?
- Use **facial expression:** facial expression replaces tone of voice for deaf people
- Use **body language** – this gives information about the way you are feeling
- Use **gesture** – to give directions, some numbers, position, shape etc

- Use **fingerspelling** (if you both know it) – often the first letter of a difficult word really helps
- **Write it down** – often the best and quickest way is to write down key words (no need to write everything)
- If one thing doesn't work, **try another way**

CATCH IT ANYTIME YOU CAN

Chapter Eleven

March 2012

The machine switched off automatically again after the extra thirty-minute programme

I was thinking how, after the confusing years of university, I had started to adapt to deafness but still found it hard, of course (I probably always will in some situations).

I had half expected to 'find love', as they say, during my years at university, but that just hadn't happened once I started to go deaf and lose all my confidence. In the years following university, it has also seemed mostly impossible, apart from the odd, brief time, to start a relationship, mainly from communication difficulties – it is not just hard to strike up conversation but people seem reluctant to realise that a disabled person is also worth getting to know! I have had people tell me they don't think anything would work out between us because I couldn't 'go to gigs' with them.

I suppose that is why I feel so lucky to have met Greg, who doesn't seem at all phased by my physical challenges and is very open to learning communication that works for us. In other relationships there's always been something I've not felt comfortable with or that there was something I needed to change about myself.

Right now, I really needed the loo after an hour and a half of the Neuro's programme but first had to painstakingly peel the surgical tape from my face and then from the back of each of the eight electrodes, cleaning each head with a piece of kitchen roll.

In the bathroom, the sun had moved around the house and was no longer shining in the window so brightly and so it was a good chance to pull the blind closed again. The task involved climbing into the bath, which was underneath the window, carefully holding the wall as I did so and pulling the cord on the blinds. At first, they rolled up instead of down because I pulled the wrong way (why did I *always* pull the wrong way first?). At least now I could avoid being dazzled another morning.

Still dozy, I made my way downstairs. It was nearly time for my favourite teatime quiz show on the telly so fetching a small bottle of the supermarket's own 'French' beer from the fridge, carrying it to the small table by the sofa and returning to the kitchen for a bag of ready-salted crisps and another piece of kitchen roll to wipe my mouth with, I settled down (bringing/carrying anything in to the lounge involved countless journeys as I could only – just! – manage one thing at a time). To combat the early evening chill, I turned on the real flame gas fire and relaxed.

The show made me chuckle and as usual I was surprised either by how little people knew of subjects I could rattle off or how much they knew on the 'obscure' things that revealed holes in my knowledge. Not a single person could name a novel by Sebastian Faulks (I had a long list as he was one of my favourite authors); the winning pair could name many films with Matthew Broderick in that I'd never even heard of, nor was I sure I could name *any* of his films at all.

Greg texted to say he'd be late so I should eat before he arrived and after the program finished, I went to make some food. My little temperamental freezer was packed with frozen fish and various frozen vegetables and I decided on smoked haddock and frozen peas mixed with sweet corn kernels. The latter I put in a large bowl to microwave as I set a pan of water on the hob to poach the fish.

The hob was gas and I turned the controls of one ring and pressed down on the ignition with the heel of my hand. It didn't light so I pressed again and again until the blue flames danced up just as I was beginning to smell the faint gas scent.

I carried a glass of water through to the lounge and went back to stir and check the veg in the microwave, which needed another couple of minutes. The fish was already done when I prodded it with a knife and just then the light inside the microwave switched off as it completed its cycle.

I lifted the fish from the pan with a large draining spoon and put it on top of the vegetables (still in the large bowl from the microwave to save on washing up), finishing with a knob of butter.

I liked this meal and had it many times as it was easy to eat when swallowing had become difficult and fish was notoriously good as brain-food, which might help with the quiz show!

After I had eaten, I carried the tray and empty bowl into the kitchen and put the kettle on. Whilst it was boiling, I took the clothes from the washing machine and hung them on the radiators in the lounge and kitchen.

Rinsing out my flask mug, I made a cup of tea to carry up to the PC on the top floor again. As I was waiting for my tea to stew a little, I thought of my book ideas once more. What I would need now, after making a note of all the other snapshots I had relived today, was some glance at life before

NF2 when I was completely ignorant to it. I wanted to include some things that I'd really loved doing that made me very much the same as many little girls.

I supposed then that I'd need something to show how and when my childhood had been interrupted and my 'NF2 life' had begun. I was very aware that I couldn't even begin to get everything into a book but I would use small cameos to give a taste of things, It didn't take me long to formulate pictures I could write about because both of these things stood out in the narrative of my life.

I guess also, if I was writing a full account of my life, then I would need to talk about how other people around me had been affected, especially my family but also my friends. I'd want to talk about how terrible it was for us all at the beginning and how we have all adapted massively and the different ways we have dealt with the traumas we've faced. Then again, that would probably be a novel in itself and might be better told from each person's own perspective.

http://NicolaFrench(NFtoo).blogspot.co.uk/

12 February 2012

Helping me feel like me

> Another very disabling part of being disabled (if that makes sense) is the feeling of not getting full information about what's happening to my body or with things generally.
>
> I can think of countless millions of helpful examples and endless disabling ones. Getting info to me takes patience, time and often money (with BSL interpreters) so added to the unsettling

thing of not getting info is the thought of me being a diva in some way to ask. Not a good feeling.

But, I appreciate and value so much the times when communication works.

Here's some very brilliant things that help in delivering information to me firsthand and allowing me to deal with it in my own way:

- Using a BSL interpreter
- Writing things down (I have had conversations with people where they will write things clearly for me when lip-reading is tough and I value them so much)
- Emailling me instead of phoning others (phoning is such a habit I realise but for a deaf person, email is fantastic. Sometimes now doctors will email me so that I fully understand)
- Using the Internet (my GP has an online service for ordering repeat prescriptions, which makes life so much easier)
- Offering text (I need to get around by taxi a lot, even for very short journeys, but I used to be unable to book. Now the local taxi firm have given me a number I can text to book meaning I can go to places as and when, much as most people take for granted everyday)
- Using BSL! (the best of the best is when I go to conferences or courses or weekends away, or coffees with friends when everybody signs

and there's no communication barriers and I
can just be there on a level with everyone as
far as communication and information goes)

http://NicolaFrench(NFtoo).blogspot.co.uk/
January 2012
Adaptation

'The survival of the fittest is the ageless law of
nature, but the fittest are rarely the strong. The
fittest are those endowed with the qualifications
for adaptation, the ability to accept the inevitable
and conform to the unavoidable, to harmonize
with existing or changing conditions.'
  Dave E. Smalley

'It is not the strongest of the species that survives,
nor the most intelligent. It is the one that is the
most adaptable to change.'
  Charles G.

'It's amazing what you can get used to.'
  We need to talk about Kevin

I like the above quotes: adapting to circumstance
can be really challenging and inevitably some days
are better than others. I do like the idea though
that those challenged by circumstances and able
to adapt, are the 'fittest' in terms of succeeding.
For me, there are days full of regret (for things

lost and things that will never be) and there are other days you feel so adapted that living in your 'new' world feels normal and expected (those are more rare!).

I saw a celebrity on TV recently who had shot to fame overnight and who said that adapting to the seismic shift in his life had been a huge challenge. He could no longer just get on the local bus or go to the corner shop for a bottle of milk without being asked to have his photo taken with someone, chased by paparazzi or at least meeting tongue-tied people who are impossible to communicate with in a relaxed way making him feel very 'other' to 'normal' people.

From the latter two challenges, I think there are many days when I feel just like him, fame at last I suppose!

It is really important to be able to adapt, even to things you might not be all that keen to adapt to.

I have, more than once, been described as 'an unfortunate woman who suffers from a severe case of NF2' (implying to me that 'I – whoever said it – am fortunate not to live in the way this woman lives and so I will help her in any way that I can think of). How much better to be described as a 'resourceful woman who is ADAPTING daily to a severe case of NF2' (implying to me that this might be one of the people I love who says, 'This woman has adapted well to something that I have never experienced and so there is a lot I can learn from her. I will support her by recognising that she has developed extensive expertise in dealing with her illness that I can learn from and help her to build up). Which do you prefer?

(My favourite is actually is 'this is Nicola' or, in situations where it is needed, 'Nicola who has a serious case of NF2'. Full stop, no judgement about my character or my life passed, just facts.)

http://NicolaFrench(NFtoo).blogspot.co.uk/
December 2 2011
Glorying

'I glory in the emotionally commonplace.'
Eva, *We Need to Talk about Kevin*

'Whoever is patient has great understanding.'
Proverbs 14:29

I can definitely identify with 'glorying in the commonplace' right now. When I am having a particularly bad eye day, it's especially hard to wake my brain up without any of the usual stimulus.

I'm also finding that, as there's so much going on with my health, I can't put my mind to much else. My head is definitely slowing down anyway (not surprising given all the activity in there!).

So anyway, I love spending time writing stories and agonising about what colour to have my nails painted the next time I get a manicure, how much I should have cut from my hair, what sort of coffee to have or who will leave 'Strictly Come Dancing' next week! As you can see from these great feats, because my illness is honing my patience (what with bad eye days and hospital waiting), my 'understanding', intellect and intellectual insights are growing every day!

Chapter Twelve

October 1987

Nicola and Emma were practising in the back of the family's brown Ford Cavalier as Dad drove along the twisting country lanes towards Harrogate. Emma's voice was richer and deeper of the two and so she had the task of singing the harmonies where Nicola had what she considered to be the easier part of singing the melody. Once, they had tried to swap parts for amusement but Nicola had totally lost the thread of the lower notes.

They were dressed in matching maroon velour outfits: skirts with identical sweatshirt jumpers. They both wore their shoulder-length hair held in slides above their ears but Emma's hair was a tumble of brown curls to Nicola's straight blond. They finished their outfits with matching knee socks and maroon sandals that they nicknamed 'clacky sandals' because they seemed to make so much noise as you walked on hard surfaces.

The competition started at 2pm and they were in plenty of time. Mum had brought bottles of orange squash and cheese sandwiches for them to eat when they got there, and they sat on a bench outside the old stone-built civic hall to eat them excitedly. As they ate, they watched others arriving and tried to guess who would be in the competition. They saw several pairs going into the building wearing smart and often matching clothes.

Mum bought out a surprise packet of Rolos for them to share and all four of them soon demolished the packet.

It had been the idea of their church choir leader, Mrs Jenkins, to train and enter them in the contest. The church choir was a small affair and Nicola and Emma were currently the star singers, although several had good voices and together they made very easy listening.

They had been going together to the Jenkins's house each Monday evening at seven for the last two months and stood together by the polished upright piano that stood by the window looking out into manicured grounds. After learning the song, they had worked on breathing exercises, singing from their stomachs or imagining themselves singing down on high notes instead of straining up to them.

Mrs Jenkins and her husband would be here today to watch and listen proudly to 'her' singing sisters.

When they went inside, they clacked in unison through the large, echoing vestibule and signs pointed them to the room that would house the competition.

It was quite a narrow room with a small stage at one end where a piano sat ready for the accompanists, leaving room by it for the singers.

It was Nicola who spotted the Jenkins camp and she led her family across the room to sit with them on the second row from the front. The chairs were made of hard dark wood and Nicola felt uncomfortable within minutes of sitting down.

'How are you?' Mrs Jenkins whispered across to the girls, 'Have you warmed up?'

'Yes, we sang in the car coming here.'

'And are you nervous?

'No, not really.'

There was silence then, followed by clapping, and Nicola looked up to see an elderly man ascending the stage. He took out notes and cleared his throat in a way expecting attention.

'Good afternoon ladies and gentlemen, boys and girls. Welcome to the fourteenth annual Harrogate music festival; please welcome Mr Chancery, the patron of the festival.'

There was more applause as an even more elderly man was helped to the stage.

'Good afternoon, it is with anticipation that I introduce the twelve-to-sixteen year age group duet competition. I myself will be judging and adjudicating the proceedings this afternoon. Without further ado, please welcome our first pair, singing 'Spring is a Lovely Lady'.

There were six other pairs listed on the programme and most were older. Nicola had only had her twelfth birthday a few months ago. Emma was thirteen (nearly fourteen) but most of the other singers were in the older half of the age group. Each pair had their names and ages listed on the sheet.

Nicola and Emma were performing sixth and so sat listening to their competitors in awed silence. The fourth pair, Laura Robson, aged fifteen, and Cathy Parks, aged fifteen, sang in Latin and they stood out noticeably for their diction and melodious singing. The two sisters were more nervous to perform after hearing them.

After Laura and Cathy had finished, the fifth pair, Sonia Bains (sixteen) and Hilary Jones (fifteen), sang something pleasant but not nearly as well presented. Then came Nicola French (aged twelve) and Emma French (aged thirteen). Standing on the stage, Nicola was nervous and suddenly forgot the first line of the song, but once the piano accompaniment started and they were encouraged by smiles from Mr and Mrs Jenkins and Mum and Dad, they took deep breaths and sang from their tummies as they had learnt.

Roses whisper good night 'neath silvery light
Asleep in the dew, they hide from our view...

Fortunately, the song didn't require difficult to reach high or low notes and they sang in delightful harmony to rousing applause.

They didn't listen so intently to the final pair but had a sense that they were not as much competition as the Latin two.

The judge took time to deliberate and the girls slipped out to the loo and burst into excited chatter.

'That was scary.'

'It was fun though.'

'Did you hear the girls singing in Latin? They were very good.'

'Yes, they will win.'

'Let's go back, he will be scoring in a minute.'

When they returned and sat down again, the patron was already on the stage intoning his delight at the quality of the contest and regretting the difficulty of his decision. He then read out his scores and comments in the order in which the pairs had sung. The fourth pair, whom most people expected to win, were awarded 16 from 20, the highest so far and told they had sung very well, only losing the harmony on one occasion. Nicola and Emma were hoping to come at least second but when their scores were read out they were awarded 18. Cheers broke out from their row. The judge said that they had sung 'enchantingly' although the choice of song was not very technically difficult so he felt they had not shown how far their skills stretched. All the same, they had surely won having beaten the 'best' pair and only Emma really listened to the scores for the final duo.

'...and finally Chloe Simmons and Erica Beaston, the winners, with a score of 19 points, you sung very accurately and the harmonies were challenging. Well done.'

There was much applause as Chloe and Erica received their prize and grinningly sang their song once more for the audience.

Outside afterwards, everyone was surprised that the Latin pair had been 'only' third and equally surprised the winners were the winners. Nicola and Emma felt slightly miffed but also very pleased with themselves especially when Dad suggested that they all had an ice cream to celebrate before going home.

May 1983

Daddy had got a new job in Yorkshire and so the French family had moved there from the Midlands last week. Their house was bigger than the last and Nicola and Emma were excited to have the top floor all to themselves. The previous owners had decorated Nicola's room in pretty blue-flowered wallpaper from Laura Ashley and there was a skylight window above her bed for stargazing.

At the moment, she was trying to learn all the times tables and so had a poster on the wall opposite her pillows with times 1 to 10 of each number up to 12. The poster was bordered with cute dogs and cats who helped her recite the tables. She was quite good on her 9 times table but still kept getting stuck on things like 6 x 7 or 8 x 8.

This morning, she was starting at her new school which she had visited a few days ago with mummy and Emma (who would be in the class above her) and watched the other children painting and drawing pictures.

She carefully chose what to wear: her favourite blue dress with buttons down the front and cream-coloured collar. Over this, she wore a navy cardigan that she and mummy had bought from Tammy Girl before they moved.

Little Lane primary school was just five minutes on foot from their new house and had a big tarmac playground and a playing field that was across the other side of the road. The school itself was a long, single-storey building mostly built of brick.

Inside was quite open plan with each classroom leading into the next through an archway. Nicola's was first on the left when you came in through the door and Emma's was the next along so the Nicola could sometimes see her in class.

The classroom had yellow walls, covered in pictures and stories the class had done. The tables and chairs were in circles and Nicola was going to be in the Dragon group with two other girls and four boys.

Her teacher was called Mrs Foster and seemed to be really nice. She had given Nicola a sticker with her name on to put over one of the pegs in the cloakroom. The sticker had a little picture of a horse on it which she thought was excellent. She had hung up her PE bag which had her name sewn on it and contained her black PE pumps, a pair of shorts and a white T shirt, both name-labelled. When they had PE in the hall, they would wear vest and pants but sometimes when it was sunny, they would play something on the grass field outside and wear their shorts. This had been explained by Mrs Foster last week.

Mrs Foster had suggested to mummy that they come just before playtime at half ten so that she could introduce Nicola to the class and then she could go outside with them all and play.

As she walked in, Mrs Foster quieted the class and had them gather round.

'This is Nicola, everybody, who I told you about earlier this morning and said that she would be coming today. Nicola has come from a different town and now lives near here. We want to make her feel happy don't we? So we need to help her today and show her where things are and play with her. Caroline, I'd like you to look after her all day, and show her what to do at dinner time and things like that. Will you show her where the toilets are and where to go at playtime?'

'I think it's playtime now, so why don't you all go outside and enjoy the sun?'

Caroline was quite a tall girl with shoulder length black hair that she was wearing in a thick plait at the nape of her neck. She bounced up to Nicola and took her arm.

'Let's be friends?' she said by way of introduction.

Two more girls, who were probably Caroline's friends came up too and asked if they could play with Nicola and they all went towards the door.

'Do you want to go to the toilet?' Caroline asked with motherly importance, 'The girls' one is just there.'

'Yes, let's see.'

'There are four toilets but don't use that one because the ghost uses it.'

'The ghost?'

'Yes, the school ghost, no one has seen it apart from me,' was Caroline's proud announcement. 'It looks like my grandma.'

Nicola didn't really know if she should believe in the ghost or not but she decided it was best to look like she did.

'Is it scary?'

'No, it just sits on the loo and then washes its hands.'

'Does it use the soap?'

'Yes and a paper towel afterwards.'

Caroline then seemed to lose interest in the ghost and instead said, 'I live near where you do.'

'Do you live on my road?'

'Yes, I saw the big lorry come last week. Your house is Mrs Cousins' house.'

'Mummy and daddy got it from Mrs Cousins, I think.'

At that moment, one of the other girls, Beth, looked round the door and asked if they were coming to play skipping and they all went outside to join the game.

After playtime, Mrs Foster told them all to sit down because it was milk time and two boys came round with an air of important solemnity and handed out small bottles of milk with blue straws. Nicola liked milk but it was warm and tasted funny.

Beth and Sam were in the Waterlily group but Caroline was in the Dragons and was sitting next to her at the table.

Mrs Foster came over to Nicola and asked if she'd met everybody. Nicola didn't know the others on her table so she shook her head.

This is Peter, Ian, Simon, Lucy, Robert and Caroline, who you know, she pointed round the table and all the children said 'hello', some shyly and others casually without much interest in the new girl at all.

Two days later, Caroline asked Nicola if she'd like to come to tea after school. Nicola's mummy said that was a lovely idea and so that day, they walked home together crossing the big road when the lollipop lady said it was safe to cross.

They walked past the newspaper shop and Caroline said she was allowed to buy some sweets there every Tuesday when Mummy gave her 10p to choose from the 1p sweets. She and Nicola both loved the chocolate logs and flying saucers and Nicola hoped that next Tuesday Mummy would give her 10p too.

They passed Nicola's house as they went up the road and she noticed that she'd left her roller boots outside since yesterday or maybe they were Emma's?

The road was a dead end on a slight hill so it would be fun to roller boot down it when she got a bit better at doing it. Caroline's house was on the other side of the road and it was newer than Nicola's with a big grass garden.

When they went in, her mummy came to say 'hello' in the hall and ask them to take their shoes off and if they would like a toasted sandwich. They said yes and went with her to the kitchen.

'Do you like raspberry jam, Nicola?'

'Yes, thank you.'

'Why don't you girls go upstairs and I'll bring your snack up in a minute?'

'OK, can we have the tray with horses on it?'

'Certainly.'

The two girls ran upstairs and Caroline gave Nicola a tour of the bedrooms.

'That's John and Mike's room, my old brothers and that's Paul's room, my baby brother, but I don't go in there because I hate them all.'

Nicola thought that she'd quite like to have a brother but she didn't really understand them.

'Do you have any sisters?'

'No, I have to play by myself but now I can play with you.'

'This is my bedroom.'

They went into a very pink room with a small desk and a Black Beauty duvet cover.

'Do you like horses? Caroline asked.

'I love them, do you like them?'

I love them.'

'Do you want to see my My Little Ponies?' and she got them out before Nicola even had a chance to answer.

'This one,' she said, holding up a light orange pony with small apples on its bottom, 'is called Applejack and she is a bit silly and knocks lots of things over. This one,' and she held a yellow pony with blue hair and bubbles on it, 'is Bubbles and she is shy and loves getting dirty so she can have bubble baths and blow the bubbles around. I only have two but I want Minty who likes green things and collects socks.'

Nicola had never seen a My Little Pony before and thought she'd ask Mummy if she could have one.

'I wrote to Jim'll Fix It last week and I'm going to go on a My Little Pony tea party with all the My Little Ponies and we can have chocolate cake and fig roll biscuits.'

At that moment Caroline's mummy came in with the tray and gave them a plate each with half a toasted sandwich on and a glass of apple juice.

'Captain Caveman is on soon,' she reminded the girls. 'Do you like that, Nicola?'

'Yes, it's funny.'

'Enjoy your food, and don't forget to bring your plates downstairs afterwards.'

When she'd gone, Nicola took a bite of her sandwich. She'd only ever had cheese toasties before, not jam ones and she really liked it but it burnt her mouth and she put out her tongue and fanned it, Caroline did the same, giggling.

'Arghhhhhhhhhh!'

'Arghhhhhhhhhhh!'

'You've got a wrinkly tongue'

' A wrinkly tongue?'

'Yes, look.' Caroline fetched a round handheld mirror and held it in front of Nicola who stuck out her tongue again.

'Weird, yuck!'

'My brother has a wrinkly willy.'

After that, they ate in silence for a time contemplating.

November 1982

Turning seven had been so exciting. Not just the prospect of a party with ten of her friends from school asking to sit next to her at tea and a big chocolate cake to eat but the fact that she was now magically old enough to join her sister at Brownies and horse riding. Most importantly of all, though, she had been allowed to start ballet classes.

Today, they were getting the results of their first exam. Most of the class, like Nicola, had their mums with them. The small changing room was even more squashed than normal as Nicola pulled her black leotard over her pink tights and put her feet in her pink elasticated leather ballet shoes (it would be a while before she progressed to satin shoes tied with ribbons at her ankles and several years before her first, painful, point shoes).

Her mum put the last few Kirby grips in her bun and finished with a wide, pink Alice band that held the tendrils neatly in place.

At 7pm, they all filed into the hall and stood around nervously. Their teacher, Madame LeStrange swept across the room, carrying a chair to the middle of the floor, where she sat down.

Madame was a theatrical ex-ballet dancer who wore long skirts and tied her thinning hair in a minute bun. 'Gather round, children.'

They all dutifully sat on the floor at her feet, mums included.

'You have all done very well; I will now read out your marks.' She held a list in front of her; putting on her half-rimmed glasses, she read,

'Susan, pass.'

'Joanna, pass.'

'Claire, pass.'

'Natasha, pass.'

'Rachel, pass.'

'Nicola and Jenny, commended.'

Nicola leant over and whispered anxiously to her mum, 'Is that better or worse?'

Madame must have heard and turned her gaze to Nicola, 'Better,' she smiled, making the other girls feel disappointed with their passes.

'But, it is all good. You have done well, girls; I am very proud. Chop chop, we must begin our class.'

The mums moved to the row of chairs at the edge of the room as Madame instructed the girls to form a circle with their arms in third position and right leg pointed 'en avant'.

Nicola carefully lined herself up with Claire who was at the opposite side of the circle, making sure her feet were turned out and her shoulders down, waiting for the music to start so that they could polka gracefully.

No music started and she heard sniggering. She glanced round but saw nothing wrong. Her eyes met Rachel's who was behind her.

'Nicola, you need to face the other way.'

She realised she should be looking at Jenny's back and not Rachel's face and felt stupid, especially with the mums grinning at her sympathetically.

She swiftly turned and re-adjusted herself as Madame pressed play on her tape recorder.

http://NicolaFrench(NFtoo).blogspot.co.uk/
Diffusion, time bombs and hindsight

'Hindsight is a double-edged sword. Too much of it and the past seems inevitable, With too little hindsight, a panoramic perspective is impossible.'
Lance B. Kurke, *The Wisdom of Alexander the Great*

When I was little, I wasn't good at doing or being anything that seemed different to other children. I wanted to have the 'right' clothes or the 'right' toys and diffuse any sense of difference. I still find myself making decisions on the grounds of whether other people will like something but everyone does that a bit, do they not?

Nowadays I can't be the 'same' as other people in many ways because of my illness. If I am in a shop, for example, I don't just chat with the person behind the till about the weather as I am paying or pass unnoticed but instead there is the inevitable song and dance involved in me finding things, communicating (or trying to at least), asking whoever is with me to help and so on. Like it or not, I am usually conspicuous because of my illness.

As a child there were a few things that I can think of that made me slightly different from others: one side of my tongue was collapsed (I guess because my – as yet undiscovered – tumour was inhibiting the nerves?), I had the cataract in my right eye so I could only see from one eye and couldn't ever do magic eye posters or things like that. Also, I had the odd, small *café-au-lait* patch on my skin.

With hindsight these were vague indicators of my NF2, just as hearing loss in my teenage years was but at the time they were just weird things that I mostly ignored. None of them was anything that would positively indicate NF2, only the 'double-edged sword' of hindsight makes me realise that they must have all been part of it.

I suppose that now then I can enjoy the 'panoramic perspective' that hindsight allows, even if my one cloudy, glare (over) sensitive eye does not!

Chapter Thirteen

November 1990

Nicola was going to take her GCSEs that year and was busy at school and spending hours with friends.

She'd had a lump on the back of my head for about the last three months. It was fairly squishy but had a solid bit in the middle that was painful if she bumped it.

Eventually, she told her mum about it and she made an appointment with their GP, Dr Evans. She went to the appointment with her best friend from school called Caroline who lived in her street.

She felt quite grown up going to see the doctor (almost) by herself and gave her name to the receptionist before she and Caroline found two adjacent seats in the busy waiting room.

Mr Evans, a tall willowish man who was looking forward to retiring next year, had a small room in the surgery. He pressed the button on his intercom and called his next patient, Nicola French. He glanced at her file; her recent visits had been for tonsillitis (he had prescribed penicillin) and a verruca.

As Nicola walked in wearing her school uniform he pointed to a worn black chair by his desk and asked her how he could help today.

'I have a lump on my head.'

'OK, let me take a look.'

At this he moved behind Nicola who was touching the spot with her hand and parted her long hair. He looked at the lump and casually suggested it was a cyst. He asked Nicola if she was 'feeling brave' and then proceeded to jab it with a needle. At that, she felt something trickling down her neck and thought he'd burst it of whatever fluid cysts have. She put her hand up to wipe the flow and found blood. Dr Evans gave her a tissue and apologised.

He was slightly taken aback himself and had no explanation for what it was. He booked her in for minor surgery to have it removed and sent her home.

She and Caroline decided to go for a cup of tea and some chips at The Coffee Pot in the small department store round the corner, chatting about school and teenaged gossip with no thought for doctors.

On the day of the op, at a small local cottage hospital, Nicola went along with her mum. When she was called in, her mum asked the doctors how long she'd be, gave her a hug and went out for a walk.

Nicola was given a local anaesthetic and laid on her stomach, feeling no pain but aware of cutting, pulling and prodding at the back of her head. She could also hear the surgeons discussing the growth.

Nicola and her family lived in a small Yorkshire town and the doctors seemed to be saying that they'd 'never seen 'owt like it!'

Nicola gave no thought to there being any further follow up; she was sent home with a few stitches and thought nothing more of it. In fact, she persuaded her mum to take her back to school so that Caroline and her other friends could admire her stitches.

November 1990

'Nicola, phone call for you.' Quite a normal occurrence (especially for a teenaged girl!)

'OK', she said, running up to the phone in the hall. The phone sat on her family's 'shoe cupboard' whose dark depths seemed to conceal the pair of whichever shoes you were searching for.

She picked up the receiver and, putting it up to her right ear, said, 'Hello?'

Silence.

'Hello?'

Silence again.

'Hi, are you still there?'

Silence.

At this she put the phone to her other ear and shifting position heard '…on Friday is that OK?'

'Oh hi, Steve,' she said, recognising the voice of someone she babysat for. 'Sorry, I missed that, can you repeat?'

Well, he was asking her to babysit on Friday and they finished off the conversation in the usual way.

That was the time she had identified as being the moment of realisation that she had completely lost the hearing in her right ear.

She wasn't really concerned; her good friend at school had just had to have her ears syringed for a build-up of wax, so she was expecting it to be something similar. She was pretty sure there'd be some simple explanation.

July 1992

It was the end of the school year and, although Nicola had had surgery and missed nearly two months of the previous year, she had managed to complete her GCSEs at the same time as her friends and was now enjoying the sixth form. Everyone was going to a ball at a hotel near to school and beforehand most people were getting together in The Swan for a drink.

Nicola was seventeen and couldn't usually get served but today Caroline, who seemed to look a good two years older than she was, had got the drinks. Most people were drinking cheap cider and Nicola followed suit although she didn't much like the sickly taste.

The pub was decorated with loud floral wallpaper that clashed with the loud floral carpet but it was so packed out that you could barely see it. As usual there were rumours of a police raid to catch the underage drinkers but again, as usual, there had not been one so far.

Nicola and her friends had been some of the lucky few to get a table and they were sitting with a group of boys who were leaving school this year having just done their A Levels,

She and Caroline had been clothes shopping last week and walked for hours from one shop to another trying things on, stopping for lunch in a chaotic McDonalds to eat cheeseburgers with chocolate milkshakes.

In the end Nicola had been persuaded to buy a pair of very short red tartan hotpants with a black Lycra vest top. She'd also got a new Rimmel eye shadow and lipstick and spent hours getting ready before coming out, painting her nails red and curling her long hair.

Caroline was now standing by the bar chatting to a boy called Ryan whom she had fancied for ages but been too shy to talk to.

Sitting in the corner, Nicola suddenly felt like she was watching everybody else laughing and talking but that she wasn't quite there herself, and had an uncontrollable urge to go outside. Shouting at the top of her voice to Kathy who was beside her that she needed some air, she put down her drink and pushed her way through the throng and out the back door into the car park.

She could still hear the throbbing music which was making her ears buzz and it had been so smoky inside that her clothes and hair stank of cigarettes.

It was raining so she huddled under her red spotted umbrella and walked quickly through the car park and across the road to a line of shops that had their windows lit up. One had a covered doorway so she sat down and pulled her knees to her chest, hugging her legs in her arms and resting her forehead on her knees. The next thing she knew, she was sobbing convulsively, great hacking sobs that went on and on.

All this: the hair, the lipstick, the nail polish, the hotpants, the cider, the flirting, seemed to have no meaning all of a sudden.

She had no idea how long she sat there oblivious to any passers-by, not caring who might see her but eventually she felt an arm around her shoulder; it was Kathy.

'What is it? You've been gone ages. I got worried.'

Nicola wiped her nose on the sleeve of her jacket and tried to say something but more sobs came out. Kathy held her more closely and they rocked gently until Nicola looked up again.

'Why me?'

'What?'

'Why me? Why do I have this?'

'You'll be OK.'

'But why me?' Nicola picked up her damp umbrella and threw it forcefully against the shop window and started crying again, more calmly now.

'Why me?' She repeated softly over and over, 'It's not fair.'

'I don't know,' was all Kathy could offer in reply. 'You'll be OK.'

Nicola laughed through her tears.

'I'm being silly, I just....'

She didn't really know what she 'just'.

'Has Caroline snogged Ryan yet?'

'No, not yet but everyone's going up to the disco now. I think Caroline and Ryan went together. Come on. Let's go too.'

'Yeah. I haven't finished my drink.' She laughed again.

'I think Zoe drank it!' I'll get you one at the Medway.'

'Thanks. Thanks Kathy.'

She sniffed again and stood up to retrieve her bent brolly and slipped her arm through Kathy's to head up to the party.

Chapter Fourteen

March 2012

With those pictures in the forefront of my mind, I remembered the follow up: the GP's suspicions, the CT scan, X-ray images of large tumours in my head, advice from doctor relatives, visits to specialist doctors, endless tests and eventually surgery, the beginnings of facial palsy, months of slow recovery, regular hospital visits and check-ups. This has all been followed by tumour growth and re-growth, more major surgery, many times of slow recovery interspersed with long periods of relative wellness and journeying through life (much more appreciated when set against the difficult times).

I knew how it could sound in a book if I didn't write carefully, in a way true to my temperament and experience. To me, my illness wasn't a tragedy that had signalled an end to life but it had added a new trajectory to my life. At the same time, I didn't want to be all saccharine and airbrushed about the challenges and emotional tumult that inevitably assailed me.

From the bombarding thoughts today I had realised something myself: I had mentioned in one of my blogs that I felt I was losing my identity as a woman and endlessly referred to 'normal' and 'proper' life as if mine wasn't. Now I feel I am comparing myself to something I *think* I should be, something I *think* other people are (when they're not necessarily) instead of just realising I am a whole woman as I am now. In a way, I am doing just what I've felt others are thinking and haven't, in fact (though I thought I had), truly accepted me as me now.

Additionally, I may not have been quite the 'me' I am without this illness, who knows?

Having said that, there is much more to disability than 'just' the physical side of it: it challenges your whole identity, relationships and dynamic of life and in some respects that side of it is more difficult to deal with than your unreliable body.

On my PC, I firstly went on to Gmail Blogger, clicked on 'New Post' and felt suddenly inspired to type a blog:

http://NicolaFrench(NFtoo).blogspot.co.uk/

March 13 2012

The best medicine?

'A cheerful heart is good medicine.'
   Proverbs 17:22

'They say laughter is the best medicine, but why does this saying persist? Because it's true. Because even though tears are necessary for some healing, laughter is what helps real growth take root. Laughter affects our minds and hearts, and these both affect our bodies.'
   http://ezinearticles.com

I've been running some research recently, trying to find the origins of some wise and enduring sayings. No one seems sure about 'laughter is the best medicine' but as quoted above, it really does help in living with serious illness.

The top quote appears in the Bible and some people have thought that it might be the origins of the truism.

I am not offering a laughter cure for NF2 and know very well that laughter isn't always the first reaction I have to things nor is it the sensible reaction to many challenges. However, I know beyond doubt that laughing when I can makes me feel better (is it endorphins? Serotonin?).

I've compiled a list of things people with NF2 are allowed to do:

1. Eat Digestive biscuits for breakfast or a bar of Dairy Milk for lunch or a big bowl of porridge for dinner (not all on the same day or you might get scurvy!).
2. Have a big hot bath at two in the afternoon or three in the morning
3. Choose friends with cars who can drive you about and like coffee (NOTE TO FRIENDS – you didn't think I actually liked YOU did you?!)
4. Take taxis for journeys of three minutes or less.
5. Have dressing-gown days or mornings when you feel low, frustrated with your body and disappointed with your restrictions (remember, this is INEVITABLE).

This is not a fully exhaustive list, add your own!

There's an interesting online article in *Science Daily* about research carried out by Melissa B. Wanzer looking at how humour definitely has positive effects on professionals, elderly people, communication in the workplace, learning and so on. It's vital to life. When something you just know by default becomes SCIENCE, it carries more strength!.

Smiling is the first step, apparently.

After I had finished writing this, I checked the time and saw that it was already almost 7pm and Greg would be here any minute but I knew he could let himself in and would hear me typing away up here.

I opened a blank Word document because, after so many 'profound insights' today I wanted to record the first line of the book that I intended to begin tomorrow. I was starting to think of how to put something together that made sense as a novel. It was difficult to think how to organise everything and especially hard to decide on what to include and what to leave to my own memories when there was so much that I couldn't possibly fit in. I started to type:

'I always open my right eye before my left for some reason…'

Chapter Fifteen

Part Two – The Others: Mum

From: pamfrench@freely.co.uk
To: nf1975@talkback.co.uk

Dear Nicky,

Thanks for emailing your book, I loved it, it sparked lots of memories for me of when you were little. I would like to read more about your childhood because we used to call ourselves 'the ladybird family', do you remember?

We had a lovely house in Yorkshire with lots of space for the four of us. You were always having friends over, it was lovely having Caroline on our street. Have you seen her recently? We were also able to fund for you and Emma to do so many things.

Do you remember at one point that we had to decide on something for you to stop doing because you were doing so much? You had the ballet classes, tap and modern classes, piano lessons, flute lessons, horse riding lessons, church choir and later the young people's theatre group. You were so talented, you seemed to be good at everything and you were such a pretty little girl. I suppose I'm gushing like a proud mother but it really was true.

We had some wonderful holidays together as a family, didn't we? I was reminded of when we went to France for your first holiday abroad when you were only about nine and Dad taught you some French like 'passez le beurre s'il vous plait' at mealtimes. He made a little book for you didn't he?

I wonder if that influenced you later when you loved French at school?

We always ate together as a family and talked about everything,

On sunny days, you and Emma would be roller booting around the garden or riding your bikes downhill, pretending they were horses.

You asked me if I'd like to write anything about how I felt when you were diagnosed with NF2. I don't think I could write anything for your book but will try to say something in this email and then maybe you can write for me?

I wasn't much older than you are now and was loving being married with two talented girls and I was like you in not seeing the implications of your symptoms although I did have underlying worries, mostly in the night as you can imagine.

When I took you for your CT scan, I was doing everything I could to be jolly and not to seem like an anxious mother but it was awful to see you in the hospital.

Once we got the diagnosis, I was just in shock. Your dad and I talked to the doctors and we weren't sure how much to tell you. They laid out for us that you had a severe case and that it wasn't going to be easy, even saying that you might be brain-damaged after the first surgery or even that there was a risk you might not get through it because your VS were so big. I know you know that now so I can say. It was numbing, surreal, like life being pulled out from under me, I can't really put it into words properly.

At the time, we tried to tell you as much as we could but wanted you to continue as positive as possible (you have always been incredibly positive). Dad and I used to cry together a lot, I would collapse and scream for you, you were and are my baby, I'm sorry if it upsets you to read that but I think now we have both matured so much and got so much better at handling all this. I think you probably know most of this.

When you went in for surgery, I couldn't eat, sleep or function and your dad and I started having problems too. (As I am sure you were aware but didn't want to write about.)

We were also worried about Emma because we naturally spent so much time with you in hospitals or thinking about you that Emma was often left to herself. We tried our best but the first years were agony. I also felt guilty with it being genetic, as if somehow I could have prevented it.

Again, I hope you are OK reading this, darling. I know we have talked about a lot of it but it gave me a sort of breakdown to see you.

Things are a bit different now and I think we both needed the time when you went away and lived down South, I needed the space as much as you did, I think.

You seemed to go through your adolescence in your early twenties, I suppose because you were dealing with so much but Dad and I couldn't talk to you or do fun things with you because you were quite snarly. Emma used to tell me I hovered around you too much and made a fuss. I think we all needed to mature and adjust and being apart helped.

When your dad died that was just another of the blows that seemed to be out of control (missiles that never missed). You haven't said much about your dad, how he was a rock and about him and me but I don't want to either really.

You're right, it WAS hard when you went travelling and I worried about you everyday but I loved getting your emails and then seeing all those photos when you got back and knowing you had experienced all that you did.

I'm so glad you have moved back up here and we can spend more time together cause I think we got a bit estranged didn't we? But now we are both so much better at coping with your illness although, of course, it will never be OK and I will always have lots of agonies for you, we are getting better with it. I don't think the pain can ever get less but it seems to get more familiar and we get better at dealing with it. I do so admire you love. It's getting harder for you now but we're doing OK aren't we?

Love from your proud mum

From: nf1975@talkback.co.uk
To: pamfrench@freely.co.uk

Oh thanks Mum, that's brill and honest and emotional. Would it be OK if I just put that in instead of re-writing it? I think it's good to be in your own words?

I haven't seen Caroline for a while but she's coming on Friday with Sam, probably go to Coffee World as per.

Love you xxx

Chapter Sixteen

André

I'll kill Nicola for saying I'm named after a pianist; I've been trying to convince people for years that my parents saw in to the future and named me after a tennis player who would one day be world number one.

Me and Nicola both liked tennis and went to Wimbledon together a few times (I still go every year). Sometimes we stayed with friends nearby and then queued or other times we won tickets through the public ballot.

In 2004, we got seats on Court Number One on the first day and saw women's world number two Lela Popova demolish unseeded Brit Jenny Webb 6 1, 6 0, and then third seeded American Hank Patterson drop a set but come on to win 6-7, 6-4, 6-4, 6-0.

One year we went to Paris to watch the qualifying rounds of the French Open where British number one Tracy Summers lost to a Czech player called Namilova, who was knocked out herself in the next round.

Nicola always liked tennis but she wasn't really a proper fan. She knew the top players whom everyone knows and watched the grand slams (though not always). She wasn't one of those people who go to Wimbledon just to have the champagne and strawberries and barely watch any matches at all though, mind you, but sometimes I'd talk about a player and could tell she didn't have a clue who they were, although she pretended that she did and nodded in agreement whenever I made a prediction. We were always very competitive and neither of us ever wanted to show an area of lesser knowledge to the other. Tennis was one of the things we talked about most.

I am speaking in the past tense because I haven't seen much of Nicola recently and we have sort of dropped out of touch since Si and I moved to London. We've set up a theatre company and run workshops and training courses for deaf and disabled people who would like to get into acting. There are limitless opportunities for a lot of people. Unfortunately at the moment, we can only get grants from people who specify that the courses are for Londoners only but we hope to expand them nationwide soon.

Having said that, I popped up to see Nic just after she'd had the surgery on her eyelids to help her eyes close better and she still had swollen black eyes like she'd been twenty rounds in the ring.

Her walking was really unsteady and communication was more difficult. Outside, I'd have to do blind-manual fingerspelling or keep silent but inside, she could just about see my signing.

We went out with Greg one evening (he seems a nice guy but not my type) and Nicola walked everywhere on his arm and sometimes mine too. She said she could get used to going out with two men.

She hadn't really changed, her sense of humour was still as dry as ever, although she did admit to not knowing about the tennis. Maybe she has mellowed with age like we all do?

At university where I was doing drama and theatre studies, I was really glad to be introduced to Nicola and we met several times a week for coffee or a pint. I used to take her to gay bars or clubs but it was hard to get chatting to anyone with Nicola there.

After the first time we met, Nicola lost my contact details and so she and her friend came to my hall of residence to ask for me. I reckon she fancied me but she swears she didn't but just felt bad about not getting back in touch.

I'm glad she did come, though, because we got to be really good friends and her NF2 for me then was a good thing because she was deaf and had learned to sign and I was born deaf but only recently learnt to sign too as I had gone to a mainstream school and grew up orally.

I don't mean her NF2 was a good thing, period, but in our uni days, her health wasn't too bad. She had unsteady balance and struggled occasionally but walked and ran fine, really (I went to see her doing the marathon). She was a bit short-sighted but mainly she was just deaf and it was good to meet another deaf person who understood how isolating it felt sometimes.

There were a few other students I'd met who called themselves deaf and talked about how hard it was but they were really only hard of hearing and didn't really understand profound deafness.

I had two more years of my course after Nicola graduated and I met Si in my second year when he came to give a talk to us, having recently finished his course at RADA. We didn't get together straightway but swapped email addresses and chatted a lot that way.

At the time, Si was living with his then partner, Shaun, but they broke up whilst I was travelling with Nicola so we got together not long after I came home.

Travelling was brilliant, although I wish we could have had a bit bigger budget because we stayed in some pretty grotty hostels and spent hours waiting for buses when taxis would have been so much quicker and easier.

It was shocking when Nic had to fly home and difficult to sort out and I had to go to Mexico on my own (scary at first but in the end helped my confidence and assertiveness). Nic emailed me that she was OK and I managed to find some internet cafes along the way to keep in touch.

Nic's invited to my birthday party in summer and will hopefully be able to come as long as she doesn't need to go to hospital again. She said travelling will probably be hard but she will bring someone to help her; hopefully Greg will come.

Chapter Seventeen

Emma

I wasn't keen to write anything for Nic's book when she first asked me but now I've been thinking about it more I will try and put something together.

Some things about me; I am older than Nic by only about eighteen months so, being close in age, we spent most of our time together when we were kids. Nic used to annoy me a lot, of course (she is my little sister) but she was my best friend too. She used to do this annoying thing when we were both cleaning our teeth of spitting out her toothpaste on my head when I was bent over the sink rinsing out my mouth but that's what sisters do and looking back it was funny really and companionable. I was so glad to have her around.

When we were teenagers, visiting our granddad who lived at the seaside, we would think we were really cool and grown up and go to the park at the end of his road carrying my ghetto blaster playing music and singing along. I suppose it was less cool that we played Bananarama and Kylie when she was still with Stock, Aitken and Waterman.

That would've been not long before they found her NF2, I suppose. When I read Nic's book, I went up to the attic and pulled out my diaries from that time and they have bought back to me how cataclysmic it was when she was first diagnosed and we were both teenagers. I can't print it because a teenaged girl's diary is not something to share but I have picked out and edited some extracts that might tell you a bit more about then..

Wednesday 1 April 1991

It's Nic's sixteenth today and we're going out for a family meal tonight at Chez Nous. I'm going to wear my black dress and new shoes and Nic's going to do a French plait in my hair like she used to.

Tuesday 14 April

God, Nic has been wearing my shoes again without asking, but it feels bad shouting at her now cos I feel I shouldn't when she's ill. I'm now in my room with the door locked from the inside so that nobody can get in. Feel a bit weird and lonely. I want to hug her but I want us to be normal too.

Wednesday 15 April

Mum, Dad and Nic left for the hospital early this morning, it's over an hour's drive, I think. Nic is having her operation tomorrow, Dad says it will be fine and I am going to see her in a few days when it's the weekend. Tonight they're staying in a hotel near the hospital as Nic might go in for her operation at eight in the morning.

It's oddly quiet in the house but I suppose I can watch what I like on telly for once. Mum took me to Tesco to get some food and tonight I had a Fray Bentos pie with HP sauce, I didn't bother with vegetables. It seems easier to think about telly and food than the real stuff.

Feel weird again, more than ever, stuck here, don't really feel I know what's going on.

Dad just phoned me, they arrived fine and Nic has her own room and she likes the chocolates I bought for her. They are allowed to take her out for dinner tonight so I think they are going for a pizza, wish I could go too. Being in hospital's not really 'fine' is it?

Thursday 16 April

People keep phoning up to ask me how Nic is and everyone at school was asking too but I didn't know, how was I supposed to know?

Dad just phoned, she is still in theatre after nearly twelve hours.

Friday 17 April

Dad phoned this morning, Nic came out of the op at 2am last night, eighteen hours. Dad says she's alright and he's driving home tonight so we can go and visit tomorrow.

I've told people at school that she's alright. Is that alright?

Sunday 19 April

When we got to the hospital yesterday, Mum and Dad took me for a cup of tea before I went to see Nic. I had bought a mixed tape I had made myself for her to listen to on her Walkman. She's gone deaf in one ear but can hear in the other.

Mum and Dad looked really tired and said that Nic was asleep and was quite poorly but that I could go and see her.

Before, they had said she was alright but she wasn't alright. There was a bandage round her head with blood on it and a mask over her mouth to help her breath, she had a drip in her arm and a catheter so I started crying but Mum and Dad told me she'd be **alright**.

I've told everyone she's alright, I hate that word.

Dad bought me home last night but I didn't feel like writing anything. When she wakes up, I am allowed a day off school to go and visit again, I don't really want to go but the same time, I want to be there all the time but I don't want to make a fuss when Nic is so ill and Mum and Dad are busy and stressed.

Wednesday 22 April

Nic is awake and has moved to a different ward. Dad has been driving to the hospital everyday but sleeping here at night, Mum has got a bed in Nic's room and is sleeping at the hospital. Dad said she has had her bandage taken off and is sitting up in bed today. I am going with him tomorrow.

Thursday 23 April

Today was really awful. Nic was OK and talking but her temperature has gone really high so the nurses were worried she has Meningitis. They said the doctor would come in the afternoon to do a lumbar puncture to check so Mum and Dad left me with Nic in the morning and went off for a walk and a coffee.

The doctor came early though so only I was there. They explained that they were going to put a needle in Nic's back to get some fluid from her spine and that I should hold her hand but Nic started crying and saying that she didn't want it because it would hurt and I didn't know what to do.

The doctor said it might hurt a bit but it wouldn't take too long and that he'd done lots before and it would be alright, everyone keeps saying it's alright..

They made Nic lie on her side and felt down her spine and then put a cross on it with yellow dye. A nurse came in and I let her hold Nic's hand. Nic was still crying and I felt sick.

When the doctor put in the needle, she screamed and said it really hurt, the doctor tried to get some fluid but nothing came out so he had to take the needle out and do it again, it took ages and Nic was still crying then Mum came back after it was finished (Dad moving the car) and Nic stopped and Mum hugged her. I started crying and the nurse had to hug me.

Wednesday 29 April

Nic came home today and is lying on the sofa watching telly. Mum has gone for a walk and Dad is in the kitchen making tea. We are having boil in the bag cod in parsley sauce, mashed potato and peas tonight because Nic fancies that. They asked me to unpack her bag and put the washing on. Then I'm going to talk to Nic.

Blimey, it was such a terrible time. I have learnt since that Nic was always particularly sensitive to any pain after anaesthetic so the lumbar puncture maybe wasn't as bad as all that.

A different time, she was coming round from surgery and dad bought her a soft toy and put it on her stomach for when she woke up but on opening her eyes she shouted, 'Ow, ow, get it off, it hurts,' and dad swiftly removed it. Things hurt in amplification.

I haven't always seen her after all her more recent ops but she assures me that the anaesthetic seems to have improved and she gets over it more quickly and feels pain less acutely.

It was so very difficult but I don't want to talk too much about what it was like for me and have missed out quite a lot from my diary about how I was feeling. Writing as a sibling, that could be a whole book in itself. I really want to talk about what happened to Nic for her book.

Nic has been teaching me some signing recently. I did a course before, not long after I got married but we lived away from Nic then so I never got to practise and it was harder but now we meet each week. I feel like I forget loads of things but Nic assures me that I'm learning fast.

Sometimes I take her out to church or other places she can't get to and meet more deaf people so I can sign more often.

Weird thing is that my eldest daughter is now the age Nic was when all this first started. Puts it all in perspective quite acutely: what Mum and Dad must have felt and what a nightmare it all must have been to deal with. Also how me and her were just emerging from being children.

I'll leave it there.

Chapter Eighteen

Greg

I was a bit shattered – it'd been a long day. The computer system had kept crashing at work so we spent most of the day without internet access and I couldn't do most of the pending jobs on my inexhaustible list.

To top it all, one of my very able team had handed in her resignation after seven years with us and it was going to be difficult to replace her with anyone who didn't need hours or days of training and weeks of supervision.

I'd barely had time to shower and change before heading off to Nicola's place. She'd texted me earlier to ask if I fancied a drink tonight and I'd told her yes but now I just felt like flopping on her sofa and watching some mindless film or other on the telly.

I'd driven her to a pub that we came to a lot called Greystones. It was really part of a hotel but I liked it as it was usually quiet. We found a table and I made sure she had the light behind her and it was on my face. It was a dull evening, fortunately, so she was out even without her massive dark glasses, (part of her disguise, she had once informed me). She still had one of her hats on.

Want what? I signed (I had learnt signing 'on the job' from Nicola).

'Well, you I suppose.' came the grinning reply.

I laughed, Drink what?

'You are signing 'who'.' Drink WHAT? She signed waggling her index finger from side to side, not rotating it as I had been. I always got the question signs muddled: Who. What, where, why, how, which, when…

'Guess.'

I knew already that she'd have half a bitter and she confirmed it as I went to the bar to get our drinks.

When I got back and sat down wearily, she reached over the table to squeeze my hand

'Are you OK?

Yes, tired. Long day. How's your eye?

'Bit better, I could see to type today, it's not quite so blurry. Comes and goes you know? I was tidying up my book.'

Despite the fact it was quiet in there, I was still straining to hear her voice because she spoke very softly or occasionally far too loudly not being able to gauge the level of sound she was making.

'I've decided to try and record other people's points of view about my NF2 and I'd like to get yours, can I ask you some questions?'

Now?

'Yeah, if you can answer in your sleepy state but if you're knackered, it can wait.'

Well, ask.

'OK.'

She pulled a notebook from her cavernous bag that came everywhere with us and opened it to a page where she'd already written some questions in big black writing that she could read.

'Right, first remind me what I'd said in my Internet profile about my illness.'

Erm, I don't think you said much just that you had some 'physical challenges'.

'So when did you find out about my NF2?'

Later, when we chatted on the web. You told me you were deaf and had NF2. I looked it up on Wiki.

'And how did you feel?'

I liked you, you made me laugh. I shrugged, I'd rather her questions were more to do with how to get Skype on her PC or how to stop her kitchen tap from dripping, I could answer that sort of thing better.

'Well, do you think it would have made a difference to you answering my profile if I had said straightaway?'

No.

'Really? It would to a lot of people.'

I'm not a lot of people.

'I know', she smiled and got my hand again.

'One more and then I'll stop.'

OK.

'Do you think you'd have ever got chatting to me in a bar?'

I don't pick up women in bars.

'Seriously. I don't, I think communication would have made it hard.'

You're probably right.

'Let's stop, you can barely string a sentence together.'

Yes. I leant forward and kissed her, smiling.

Truth was, I loved her and that was the main thing.

Come on, let's get going, I'm hungry.

'Yes, me too.'

Caroline

My name is Caroline Barker and I have known Nicola since forever really. Actually, I remember that first day we met at primary school too.

When Nicola came in and our teacher, Mrs Foster, introduced her, she looked a bit shy but like someone I'd like to be friends with.

Like little girls do, we fell into friendship right away.

When it came to story time, the whole class sat cross legged on the mats in the book corner while Mrs Foster read to us. Several girls asked Nicola if they could 'play with' her hair, which was a waist length sheet of shiny blonde that somehow made us want to touch it. The girls put minuscule plaits in it and then brushed them out with their fingers.

Nicola kept her hair fairly long for many years but lately she's been lamenting to me that her hair's 'died' and won't grow beyond her shoulders without turning to straw. She had it all cut off recently like when she and André went travelling. It wouldn't surprise me if dry hair is linked with NF2 as most things seem to be.

I have tried to think what it's been like to have a seriously ill best friend but it's hard. I mean most of the time, Nicola is just Nicola. It is getting harder now not to see the illness as her sight and mobility affect day to day so much.

I read a book several years ago (I forget the name but it was very good). At the time, it had little significance beyond being a good read but remembering it now and seeing Nicola, I feel a bit eerie.

At the start, it appeared to be about ordinary kids at a boarding school but later it became apparent that it was much more sinister than that.

They were, in fact cloned or, at least 'bred' specifically to donate their organs to the 'real' population and, once they reached maturity, began to gradually donate parts of themselves until they 'completed' (i.e. died).

It sounds really maudlin but it's felt like that with Nicola sometimes. She calls it her 'onethingafteranother' life and it sometimes feels like she is jumping through hoops trying to adapt as various functions of her body eke away. She loses the ability to do one thing so she finds something else and then, after a while, she can't do that either and so it goes on. It's like the hoops are getting smaller and smaller and harder and harder to find a way through.

The greatest thing I have learned over the years is that we humans can deal with far more than we would think possible when it is thrown at us. If ever I think of NF2, the word that enters my head is resilience.

CATCH IT ANYTIME YOU CAN

Epilogue

I was quite pleased with my book when I'd got it all together. Caroline had said she didn't really want to write much or answer any questions about the book and I totally understand. I think what she's written is really good though and far more intelligent than I expected (Hi, Caroline!!). In fact, seeing things through other eyes and reading these all together has made me cry and get goosebumps.

Of course, there is a lot that I haven't included. For example, I didn't write about the time I was sent for a full body MRI scan just after my initial diagnosis and it showed several tumours down my spine and in my brainstem as well as the ones in my head. The doctor that we saw to get the results knew nothing about NF2 and sat us down and gravely told us he was sorry but the brainstem one looked inoperable and he couldn't see I had more than about ten years to live (I was eighteen!).

I didn't write about things like that because I have no words to describe how it was.

I haven't written enough about being deafblind and the emotions attached: the grieving and spontaneous bouts of unprompted weeping, the panic attacks I experience when communication is not working. I haven't written about them because I am still in the process of adapting and getting accustomed and it all feels a bit raw and confused to put into words yet.

I know how much it helps to be positive but I no longer think of describing the reality as negative, it's just how it is and, stupidly, I used to feel guilty for sharing it. Silly old me!

There's also loads and loads of other stuff I had to miss out, the normal 'messiness' of life. I'd hate Greg to think that I have waited thirty-seven years to meet a man I care about (he's far too big-headed already!) nor should Caroline and André think they are my only friends! I know that they don't, but I hope anybody who reads the book will know too.

If I truly wrote my life, it would take approximately 654 books of incoherent ramblings. I hope what I've ended up with here is more of a comprehensible story.

Most authors are never happy with their books and I guess I understand that feeling! Sometimes I'm not even sure if the things I HAVE said are said quite right. I have to draw the line somewhere though and, hey, I can't tell you how brilliant it feels to be an author and not a poor, unfortunate patient (I know it's just another label that says nothing about me but at least it doesn't imply judgements or assumptions).

Anyway back to the present…

I went to the gym again today and Lorraine from Social Services came with me. Good job because I could barely read the machines and they've got some new things I didn't know how to operate.

It was also useful to see her because I'd had some post that I couldn't read and so she was able to tell me what the letters said (there's some fantastic technology out there to help with that kind of thing and I really must investigate). One of the letters was for a follow-up MRI scan next month to see how things are going.

Yesterday, I went to see the Olympic torch being carried through my mum's town but it was fairly sunny so I nearly missed it. There was nowhere to sit down so I was leaning against a lamp post for nearly an hour waiting and by the end, my legs barely functioned, they were so tired from all that standing up.

I had a good cry when I got in as all that standing around, not seeing well and then struggling to walk the five minutes back up to Mum's house (even with support) all got too much for me. I have been known to think of times like that as me quitting or admitting defeat but really they are just me showing that I'm reassuringly human.

I'm prattling on now, aren't I? But I don't really know how to finish this book because I've already 'finished' it once when I wrote the first bit. I recently wrote some new blog posts and I think I'll finish with them again, although there's a blog I'd like to write about the relativity of 'good' news and how good news for me now is when my MRI scans show several fairly large tumours but the doctor says he doesn't need to operate on them yet and will scan them again in a year's time.

Well, that one's pending but I already wrote these blogs:

http://NicolaFrench(NFtoo).blogspot.co.uk/
2 June 2012
Humankind and kind humans

> 'And as I've gotten older, I've had more of a tendency to look for people who live by kindness,

tolerance, compassion, a gentler way of looking at things.'
   Martin Scorsese

'A part of kindness consists in loving people more than they deserve.'
   Joseph Joubert

'A laugh, to be joyous, must flow from a joyous heart, for without kindness there can be no true joy.'
   Thomas Carlyle

'Yet do I fear thy nature,
It is too full o' th' milk of human kindness
To catch the nearest way'
   Macbeth Act 1, scene 5, 15–18

In *Macbeth*, an ambitious lady Macbeth is criticising her 'milky' husband for not having the mettle to commit murder and then seize the crown but I, on the other hand, adore 'milky' people!

   I wonder if I get to see more of it as my health gets harder for me to manage? I really do see it every day whether from strangers, slightly known acquaintances, friends or family. There are so many things I couldn't do without others giving time, energy, wisdom and love.

Forget those pesky, difficult-to-open pints of milk, I often seem to get my milk by the bucket-load and it gives me a warm, satiated glow! Sometimes people's capacity for kindness never ceases to amaze me.

http://NicolaFrench(NFtoo).blogspot.co.uk/
6 June 2012
SUNSHINY DAYS (or afternoons/hours/minutes)

'Hope need not mean expectancy.' (of improved circumstances?)
George Watts

'Hope is a good thing, maybe even the best of things and good things never die.'
(Andy's letter to Red at the end of *The Shawshank Redemption*)

'The sun will come out tomorrow
Bet your bottom dollar that tomorrow, there'll be sun…'
Annie

'It's gonna be a bright, bright sunshiny day.'

There is a painting I like by George Watts in which he depicts a blindfolded woman clutching a wooden lyre with only one string left intact. She is hunched, with her head leaning towards the instrument, perhaps so she can hear the faint music she can make with the sole remaining string. As quoted above, George Watts wants to show that music can come even when situations look dire.

In the book I have been writing, I wrote that I didn't want to be all saccharine and airbrushed (or 'Pollyanna-ish') about NF2 but I just had a nice thought extending the often used idea of the sun as a metaphor for life. It is leaning a bit towards Pollyanna-ishness but also runs along similar lines to the thinking of George Watts as he was painting.

On bright, clear days we can enjoy the sun's warmth and caress on our skin but there are many cloudy, often stormy days when the sun is nowhere to be seen (in the UK anyway). However, it's still there doing its thing behind the clouds and when they clear, we get to feel the sunshine again (and even I can enjoy a metaphorical sun!).

With risk of sounding like Annie's slightly pessimistic cousin, despite everyone experiencing clouds and storms in life, the sun will come out... *sometimes*.

I'm not talking about Christian hope of eternal life or, indeed, any belief in an afterlife (I know that's down to personal faith). I mean in general, every day. As with a British summer, the sun's appearances may be rare or fleeting, sunny spells may be very brief amongst the thick clouds and they may not be in places you would expect to see sunshine nor easy to spot, but the sun WILL shine. My advice? Catch it anytime you can! x

Author's Note

This book is semi-autobiographical and the character of Nicola is largely based on my own experiences. I have, however, included episodes in Nicola's life that have not been part of mine or doctored, combined and set other episodes out of sequence. In writing the book, it became obvious that life is far too complex and inconsistent to fit into a coherent story!

Some events or opinions reflect experiences of people I have met who have NF2 or other disabilities.

The genesis of this book was a blog that I started in 2011. Writing the blog gave me confidence to attempt something more in depth, helped me to envisage an outline idea for a book and led me to see that I love writing!

Some of the posts printed in this book are taken almost directly from the blog and others are written to meet the purposes of this book and have not yet been posted online.

Other characters, although inspired by people who have been part of my life, are fictional and do not represent people's true opinions or thoughts. All names and most of the biographical details are invention.

Some are an amalgamation of several people I have known through life. Caroline, for example, represents many of my friends. The flashback of meeting her is not real and combines many disjointed memories from childhood.

CATCH IT ANYTIME YOU CAN

Neurofibromatosis type two (NF2): a brief summary

Dr Sue Huson, Consultant Clinical Geneticist, Neurofibromatosis Centre, St Mary's Hospital, Manchester

When Anna asked me to write about NF2 in the book I felt very privileged. I have to say up front that reading the draft Anna sent me taught me a HUGE lesson. I first met Anna in 2012 as she was gradually readjusting to increasing problems with her vision and mobility. At that stage she already had lost most of the function of the nerves that supply the muscles in the face. Her vision was limited to one eye which performs variably depending on how sore her cornea is. So with no facial expression, being deaf and with poor vision most of the cues we rely on for communication are gone. I have been working with people with NF2 since 1981 and it is still too easy to forget that no facial muscle movement does make you seem a bit 'slow'. Also to communicate with deaf people takes time – it is so easy in a busy clinic to say 'I will tell your family what will happen next' and cut out the main person.

Anna always has a BSL interpreter with her at clinic and so within a short time the understanding she has of NF2, her sense of humour and determination became clear. Even then, I did not take the time to find out who Anna the person really was and all the things she has achieved DESPITE her NF2. So this has changed how I practise, I make much more effort to read the full medical records and learn about people from our NF2 nurse team, who are able to visit people at home, BEFORE clinic.

So for me what is important about this book is the journey Anna has been on adjusting to losing her hearing, looking different and going from a marathon runner to someone who needs a taxi for a five minute journey. In our busy world it is too easy to 'judge' someone on first appearance and not take time to know them. I am not sure the book needs a 'medical bit' but we thought a few questions and answers about NF2 may be appreciated by some readers. So here goes... I won't begin to compete with Anna for using quotes from literature!

What is neurofibromatosis (NF)?

NF is the collective term for a group of genetic conditions that predispose people to develop benign tumours on the nerves. For many years Doctors lumped the different types of NF together but as Doctors began to specialise in NF care and MRI scans became routinely available it became clear there are two main types of NF – NF1 and NF2. What makes them different is that in NF1 the nerve tumours are neurofibromas and in NF2 they are schwannomas. In NF1 the main part of the body affected is the skin and only a proportion of people get tumours of the brain and spinal cord. In NF2 the nerve tumours are schwannomas and the place nearly everyone with NF2 gets them is on the eighth cranial nerve- the nerve that connects the ear to the brain and is essential for hearing and good balance. The long used name for these tumours was acoustic neuromas but over the last twenty years we have gradually switched to calling them Vestibular Schwannomas – this is what they really are, schwannomas that develop on the vestibular branch (the branch supplying the part of the ear involved in balance).

Some of you may be thinking but hang on, I know someone who had one of those and it was only on one side and they were much older than Anna when it was picked up. This is correct, vestibular schwannomas can occur in any of us and usually develop after the age of fifty and only affect one ear.

What causes NF2?

NF2 is caused by a mutation (spelling mistake in the genetic code) in the NF2 tumour suppressor gene. The genes are the messages for life; we all have about twenty thousand pairs of genes and they are in every cell of the body. In the cells the genes are packaged on chromosomes and the NF2 gene is on chromosome 22. We get one gene of each pair from our Mother and one from father. In each part of the body different genes are switched on at different times so we have genes important during our development in the womb and others which we need to keep different parts of the body working. The genes code for different proteins which are the chemical messengers in the cell that work together so that the cell can grow at a normal rate and do its job in a given part of the body. The NF2 gene produces a protein called Merlin. Merlin has several jobs in normal cells which include making sure the cell works properly in connection with neighbouring cells; another job is making sure the internal cell structure develops properly and finally it is involved in pathways that control how quickly cells grow and divide.

When we look at the genes in different kinds of benign and malignant tumours we find that one or more genes are not working properly. One group of genes that cause tumours are called tumour suppressors. For a tumour to form both copies of the gene in the tumour cell will have a mutation that has caused them to stop working. If a cell only has a mutation in one Nf2 gene it can still do its job and no tumours develop. When we look in vestibular schwannomas we find that in the tumour cells there are mutations in BOTH copies of the NF2 gene. When someone gets an isolated vestibular schwannoma the mutations have developed during their lifetime. We are all walking around with some mutations in some cells of the body. They arise because when a cell divides the twenty thousand pairs of genes are copied in to the daughter cells and mistakes sometimes happen. It is like writing out twenty thousand words and not making a mistake. However, many of these mutations never cause a problem; it is only if they happen in a particular gene at a time when that gene is essential for the cells normal function.

Someone with NF2 however is born with one copy of the NF2 gene not working in all the cells of their body. So they only need one more miscopy to happen and they will get a tumour. So in NF2 we see vestibular schwannomas on both hearing and balance nerves developing at a younger age than in the general population.

So how is NF2 inherited?

About half the people with NF2 have inherited it from their Mother or Father and the other half are the first person in the family. In them, NF2 the mutation in an NF2 gene occurs when the egg or sperm are made or during the first few cell divisions in the embryo. If you have NF2 there is a 50:50 or one in two chance of passing it on to your children. Some people who are the first person in the family with NF2 may have a smaller risk than this because they only have the NF2 gene change in some cells in their body. The technical term is they are mosaic for the NF2 gene.

How is NF2 diagnosed?

In people with no family history like Anna, NF2 is most often diagnosed when they develop hearing or balance problems and a Doctor does a brain scan to check the hearing nerves. Since the NF2 gene was isolated in 1993 we have been able to confirm the diagnosis with genetic testing. In someone with NF2 the gene test will nearly always find the mutation in one NF2 gene. We often also test tumour tissue to assist in diagnosis.

The big advantage genetic testing has brought is for people with NF2 who are planning a family or who have children at 50% risk. Some people decide they would like to avoid having a child with NF2 and have preimplantation or prenatal genetic diagnosis. For people with children at 50% risk we discuss with the family the best time to test. We usually plan to do it at the time when the children with NF2 would start having scans around the age of 10. The children who have not inherited the gene do not need any scans.

Can schwannomas grow on other nerves in NF2?

The answer to this is yes. All the nerve fibres in the body have Schwann cells around them. They are important for keeping the nerve fibres working properly. You could liken a nerve to an electric wire and the Schwann cells are the insulation around it. When the NF2 gene stops working in a schwann cell that cell starts to grow and divide out of control and a tumour develops. So people with NF2 can get schwannomas on any nerve in the body, we still don't know why they particularly affect the hearing and balance nerve so often.

Can other tumours develop in NF2?

Another yes, but the schwannomas are the most common. One way to think about it is that NF2 tumours tend to develop in the tissues that line our nervous system – so the Schwann cells are around nerves. A working NF2 gene also seems important in two other types of cells that line the nervous system. These are the meningeal cells – the meninges are the outside lining of the brain and spinal cord – so loss of NF2 in a meningeal cell causes tumours called meningiomas to develop, these are another form of benign brain tumour. The final type of tumour is called an ependymoma which arise in ependymal cells that line the fluid filled cavities in the centre of the brain (ventricles) and the narrow canal at the centre of the spinal cord. These are the least common type of tumour in NF2.

Anna had a cataract in one eye, is that part of NF2?

We think the NF2 gene must be important in eye development- both in the lens and the nerve layer at the back of the eye. When we look at the lens of children with NF2 many of them have subtle changes that don't affect vision. Some have fully developed cataracts and unless these are picked up and treated early the eye won't be able to see. Another way vision can be affected is when the nerve layer at the back of the eye does not form properly and forms abnormal swellings that can affect vision. Of course, if a parent with NF2 has a child then we advise getting the eyes checked early on but when you are the first person in the family changes may not be picked up for several years.

In some people with NF2, the nerves supplying a part of the body may stop working and no obvious tumour is found – this is called a neuropathy. Fortunately it affects only 5-10% of people with NF2. What makes this and eye problems difficult are that if you have a condition that can affect your hearing and balance, these are much worse to cope with if your sight or the strength of an arm or leg are already affected.

So why was Anna's NF2 only diagnosed when she went deaf?

This is because when Anna was a child most Doctors still thought of NF1 and NF2 together and the studies which clearly separated them were only just starting. The eye changes only recognised as part of NF2 in the late 1980s. Professor Evans, who leads our clinic in Manchester, published the first large UK study of NF2 in 1992.

Even now some people are diagnosed late because in NF2 the vestibular schwannomas can be very large before they affect hearing. The problem then is the tumours are pressing on the brain and so treatment becomes essential, it is very hard for someone with good hearing to accept they need an operation that will make them deaf in that ear.

What treatments are there for vestibular schwannomas?

As vestibular schwannomas are benign tumours there is no need to treat them unless they are causing problems. So for quite a few people with small tumours and good hearing the tumour growth is monitored on scans along with hearing tests. At the other end of the scale if the vestibular schwannomas are large and pressing on the brain, then surgery becomes essential. The problem for the surgeons is that the facial nerve runs along side the vestibular nerve and so it is easy to damage this when removing the tumours. The risk of this is related to the size of the tumour – the bigger the tumour the bigger the risk. Fortunately there have been big improvements in surgical techniques and the surgeons now monitor the facial nerve and check it is working throughout the operation.

The other big development, that was not available for Anna, has been the development of cochlear and brain stem implants so that although the hearing nerve is damaged when the tumour is removed, an implant can be used to give the person some hearing. The sound through an implant is not exactly the same as normal sound but it means you can hear where sounds are coming from and so can turn to someone talking to you. So lip reading and the implants work well together.

Another option to stop the vestibular schwannomas growing is a special form of localised radiotherapy called radiosurgery. This has advantages over surgery because there are far less risks and in people with hearing there is a chance it will not be affected. The limits are that the vestibular schwannomas have to be less than 3 cms in diameter and it does not stop all of them growing.

What about other NF2 tumours?

When we scan people with NF2 we may see a lot of other tumours but over the years they do not grow or cause problems. So for other tumours we monitor them and usually recommend surgery or radiosurgery only if they are growing and causing symptoms.

What about drug treatments for NF2?

Since the NF2 gene was isolated in 1993 the main research focus has been to understand how the NF2 protein works in normal cells and what goes wrong in NF2. Researchers can see that certain chemical pathways in NF2 tumours are overactive and so clinical trials are now being done to look at drugs that will control this. The first drug that has been shown to be good at controlling schwannoma growth is called bevacizumab (Avastin). It works particularly well in patients where the tumours are growing quickly. It also seems to prevent the hearing getting worse and in some patients the hearing has improved. We are finding that this is a particularly useful treatment for teenagers and young adults so that they can avoid the need for major surgery whilst finishing school, college etc. The only draw back is Bevacizumab only works for schwannomas and not meningiomas.

Coordinated care for NF2

We have been fortunate in England that since 2010 NF2 care has been coordinated though a national service. Professor Evans' studies showed that people with NF2 did much better when treated in a clinic with a special interest in NF2. Along side these studies the UK NF charity (the neuro foundation) acted as a voice for people with NF2 about what was most difficult for them, not only about their health care but also what was really useful when you lost your hearing. The charity funded two meetings about NF2 care which Professor Evans led and a model of care for NF2 was developed. NF2 care is now coordinated through four centres in Manchester, Cambridge, London (Guys and St Thomas') and Oxford. In each centre there are a team of specialist Doctors, nurses, hearing therapists and balance physiotherapists. The service also works with the charity Hearing Link who offer a variety of courses and support systems for people with adult onset hearing loss.

Back to Anna...

None of the developments in NF2 care or the clinical research would be possible without Anna and other NF2ers who have shared with us their experiences and helped with various studies. The book is another major contribution that will help everyone involved with NF2.